i

Narratives From The Lockdown

Narratives From The Lockdown

G G Howells

For my Wife and girls

Contents

Prologue: The Fountain of Shame

Spring 2020.

At least we were blessed with some beautiful weather.

I sat in my garden and I looked at my little water fountain attachment. I had noticed it. I knew I owned it - because I had bought it. But now I watched it.

It was a cheap little solar panel plate with a small water pump concealed underneath it and three different sprinkler attachments that fitted on the protruding neck, giving me the incredibly considerate option of three different variations of spray for me to marvel at and enjoy. I could choose from a small sprinkler trajectory, slightly wider sprinkler trajectory, and slightly wider than that sprinkler trajectory.

It fitted nicely into my stone birdbath that my Grandad Ralph had given me with a fair degree of ceremony a few years ago. He had owned it for several years, perhaps ten, and had probably paid over a hundred quid for it. To be honest it had not really established itself anywhere specific in the garden and had been constantly moved around hoping it would click somewhere. Between the months of September and March its chief role had been a makeshift anchor for the trampoline – no doubt protecting the appearance of many fence panels through the wet, windy winters.

It stood about three feet tall, but the stonework from the side elevation looked brand new and quite striking – very similar in appearance to the limestone they used in the architecture of many of the buildings in Bath. The warm, honey colouring that gave the historic town such a distinctive appearance was present here too. The 'Bath stone' could be sawn up, or squared, in any direction which had been used to create beautifully unique, mosaic-like brickwork patterns. Given the birdbath's girth of less than a foot at its narrowest point at the top, this was probably the perfect material for the job.

Standing over it, however, revealed its true age. Testament to the amount of harsh Welsh weather conditions it had withstood, the stone bath base that had hopefully delighted and ensured the hygiene of so many birds over the years, was no longer an inviting proposition. Full of cracks, fissures and pitting, the once ornate and probably pricey bird bath, had truly begun its decay.

Now looking more like a well-preserved Roman relic than the crown jewel of a middle-class garden centre, the top part had seemingly disintegrated into minute rust coloured pieces of grit. I would certainly not consider shedding my undergarments and slipping into it in this condition and judging by the low levels of activity it saw, the birds evidently felt the same way. In many ways, it was the antithesis of my inflatable hot tub that sat next to it which, despite its arguably obnoxious appearance, in contrast, did offer a comfortable and relaxing bathing experience.

Noticing this made me reconsider something. Whilst I have lived in this house, I have always had (what I felt were) particularly noisy birds in the trees behind my garden. All this time I was enjoying what I thought to be beautiful, and tuneful birdsong - but maybe this was not the case. Maybe, in reality, they have been lining up to scold and heckle me from the safety of their treetop; vainly trying to cajole me into action. 'Buy some concrete and resurface your fucking bird bath you bastard', perhaps.

On the underside of the small pump were four very small suckers, designed to stick the base of whatever ornament you wanted to convert into a small fountain. They would not stick to the concrete floor of the bath – far more suited to a plastic surface, and certainly not in this condition anyway. Instead, it floated around on the two centimetres (at its deepest) of water the bath could hold at capacity.

It was not a huge help that the bird bath was placed on a drain cover which was not a level surface. This meant that the water collected on one side, enticing my altruistic plastic friend to drift the few inches across and follow suit. But nature, manifesting itself through its most intuitive element, evidently had darker intentions. No doubt eagerly anticipating the small modicum of revenge it had planned for my crude oil-based abomination that had played its part so well in ravaging the planet.

Unless centred in the birdbath, the undeniably weak jet of water that was projected out of the fountain would be shot over the side of the bird bath and down on to the drain cover, preventing it from being constantly recycled and thereby cruelly denying the contraption to fulfil its sole purpose for existence. It happened much more quickly in even the slightest breeze as the wind would act as a catalyst for this process, making it capable of emptying the birdbath in mere minutes.

Once the water has been displaced, my gadget eventually becomes shipwrecked; left high and dry on a forty-five-degree angle against the side wall of the birdbath, having sealed its own fate. It avoids eye contact as it just sits there looking foolish and red-faced by this wilful act of self-sabotage that it succumbs to every time. To punish it, I leave it there for longer than necessary until I fill it up again using my watering can, knowing that it won't be long until it drifts to its doom again. But then again, I reconsider.

Perhaps I am the one being punished for not placing it on a level surface in the very first instance. Or maybe it is in cahoots with nature – each having a motive, a hidden agenda, a reason for disturbing my peace and teasing me so. The contraption: bitter and vengeful for enslaving it, shipping it across the other side of the world and then putting it to work in torrid conditions. Nature: upset at me for purchasing the contraption, thereby propagating the gratuitous manufacture of unnecessary plastic things. Somehow though, they had managed to look past their differences and unite toward a common goal. It was a lesson to us all, really.

No, it has become quite clear that both of them are laughing at me, as I get up and down to fill it with water; the price to pay if I am to continue to listen to its light-footed, watery pitter patter. Like the sound of pissing when the sole reason that you have made an attempt could be filed under 'might as well' since you have stopped at the services and have at least another couple of hours driving ahead of you. But I continued to play along with the foul charade,

4

nonetheless, ever more certain that I was being ridiculed. Ridiculed for going to the lengths to firstly make the purchase, the time spent anticipating its arrival with an uneasy mix of excitement and trepidation for two solid weeks, and then not even having the prescience of mind to utilise it in the prescribed and advised manner.

Now I feel somewhat red-faced and angry that I did not wise up to this profound truth sooner, but I keep this shame to myself. Unloading this burden on others would be unfair. They will not understand the depths of my anxieties anyway. I will have to punish myself for this in some suitable way. I will drink the nondescript French lager tonight instead of the Stella. It is no less than I deserve.

But I had to conquer this anguish. Even though it totally embodied mass-market consumer tat, and seemed hell bent on colluding with nature to bring me down, I liked it. It was a nice purchase that provided a gentle warm feeling when it served as the backdrop to sunny days in the garden. I knew I could make this work and restore the equilibrium. I must move it.

I carefully cradled my device, and lifted it from the small grit filled reservoir, and placed it on top of the hot tub. I could hear the pump still whirring after being placed on this barren, waterless surface. I needed to work quickly, but the sound of the dry whirring added extra pressure and brought about a sense of panic. In my head I could hear it calling out to me: 'I can't breathe.'

I ignored established lifting protocol, hastily bent over, and gripped the heavy stone birdbath; one hand on its base, and the other on the surface. I heaved it up to chest height, and began a slow, deliberate journey across the garden with my feet wide apart to cushion the impact of each step. As I reached the decked area in the corner, it quickly became apparent to me that I needed to employ the same level of might to place the birdbath into position, as it took to lift it in the first place. Too fast or - worse still – dropped, would be disastrous and surely smash through one, or even two of the deck boards.

I leaned over to despatch the birdbath gently on the front corner of the decking between two potted Buxus balls. It went down sweetly. But now was not the time for me to stand back to analyse and admire its new feature position. I turned and raced across the lawn to retrieve my gasping contraption. It was still whirring. Its rhythm, flawless. I grabbed my watering can and took them both over to the new level grounded location of the birdbath that offered my fountain attachment so much sanctuary. I placed it in, and used my healthily resourced watering can to replenish the bowl.

It started spluttering back into life, spitting out small droplets of water as I obscured its energy source with my looming shadow - but I was not out of the woods yet. It still did not secure to the base; a combination of the poor concrete surface and its somewhat impotent rubber suckers. As a result, it still floated around dispersing the water over the sides. I looked around and grabbed a fistful of small decorative pebbles from the stone landscaped area to my right and arranged them in a circle around my now raspberry blowing plastic friend. It worked. My device remained within the confines of the circle without obstructing the passage of water.

I stepped back to observe and allow the solar panels to bathe in the sunlight. This was the area of the garden that received the maximum amount of sun in a 24-hour period. It was perfect and transformed the fortunes of all its components. The device - cheap and tacky looking on its own, now revelled proudly in its new position. The birdbath had lived a perpetually displaced existence prior to the arrival of its new companion; never fitting in anywhere over the last few years of its life and only being recognised as useful for its weight. Now it had finally fulfilled its true purpose. Even the pebbles; plucked from a faceless obscurity amidst a sea of pebbles bereft of any individuality and thrust on to centre stage. It was a real 'rags to riches' tale for all the players.

Now I watched it. As I stared, I observed the life cycle of the droplets. They would shoot upwards in unison before exploding into multiple offshoots and beginning their more leisurely descent into the gene pool from whence they came. That in turn created new beginnings. Millions more droplets being created the same way, each meeting the same end, providing the raw materials for future generations to continue with their futile and ultimately ill- fated journey. And on, and on, and on.

But stood in its new permanent home, in full flow, my stupid little plastic device now reminded me; it wasn't about the end of the journey, finished with the faintest of splashes. It was the journey itself. The journey upwards was fast paced, and fraught with excitement about reaching the best heights it could. When contentment is reached at the pinnacle, the perspective changes. The pace becomes somewhat more pedestrian as you realise that enjoying the gentle ride down and landing safely should be the priority.

Sometimes there is a misjudgement and you hit the drain. Sometimes the wind picks up and there is really nothing you can do.

For me, this consumeristic piece of tat from China was somehow able to embody this journey, and so many other aspects of life.

But it was because of something else - that had also originated from China – that had lead to me sitting here considering all of this in the first place.

The effects of which will transform a generation.

Some of the consequences of which could last forever.

It was the 2020 lockdown.

The Hallucinating Penis

I am Prince Albert II of Monaco – a sovereign state and country on the French Riviera. I am Head of State, and Head of the princely house of Grimaldi. I am sure you know who I am; having seen me on the TV or read about me in the newspapers.

As we were a principality for many years, it was decided that we did not need a King or Queen. It's a tradition we have continued – though, basically, I'm as good as a King. So, think of it like that. If anyone wanted further proof, then they could look at the many commemorative coins my face has appeared on.

I am one of the wealthiest royals on the planet, and as you would expect, with this territory comes the opportunity to be a bit of player too. I lived the bachelor life for a long time – much to everyone's concern (bore off) – and had a string of hot girlfriends. Models, actresses – well known ones too. Proper A Listers.

I was in fact inundated with offers of courtship. And I sampled many offers, to be sure. But I was always only ever testing the waters. Looking. Searching. For that special someone who could represent our House, our Country in the best possible light. I went out on these, often, late night endeavours when I was weary, tired...even run down. And I did it – all for my people.

Naturally, this attracted some envy, and the rumours eventually surfaced that I must be 'gay'. I read it many times in the newspapers. It didn't worry me. I could take the taunts, knowing that my subjects would appreciate the long game in the future. In fact, I found it less tedious than I did when I was being relentlessly asked about when I would be married. Instead, during interviews, the journalists would show a little more restraint. Rather than tipping me the wink and then delving straight into asking me about who was the 'special lady in my life at the moment', it just didn't come up for a period of time. Being considered gay for a short while was something of a welcome change of pace.

I own casino's, hotels, restaurants, nightclubs, yachts – you name it. Most of them located in Monaco where all the stars and celebrities like to come and hang out. That is how my Dad basically met my Mum. Before she was Princess Grace of Monaco, she was an actress, known as Grace Kelly.

My family keep having to have heirs – or 'dynastic offspring', according to Wikipedia – or else sovereignty over the Grimaldi realm would have to be handed back to France. I'll be making sure that never happens. In fact, I had the treaty revised almost 20 years ago to include adoptive heirs, that should sort it – lol !

I eventually got married. Had a couple of kids. There are a couple more out there too from my younger, more carefree days. Although the paternity tests came back as positive, they could never have an official royal status as they were born out of wedlock. Illegitimate. What a horrible bloody word to label someone. I have always thought that; it really riles me. Perhaps I have one more treaty amendment in me yet. Baby steps.

I've done some other stuff too. Too much to list, but amongst them, I've completed an expedition to Antarctica, represented Monaco five times in the Winter Olympics (two man AND four-man bobsleigh), and founded a zoo. I served in the French Navy and I've won all sorts of accolades for my work highlighting environmental concerns. And can I point out that this was WAY before that young Swedish girl I see on TV and in the papers, was a twinkle in her Dad's eye. I just don't like to go on about it.

I don't mind admitting that I have had a decent start in life. Better than many, I'll grant you. But it's no free ride. I have still worked hard to keep everything I've got and push on further. I could have frittered it all away. Sold out to the French! Handed back sovereignty. But no! I resisted and continued to build something amazing. Beautiful. Full of riches. Paradise. I made it what it is today. And life here is a dream.

Well - it was.

A few weeks ago, I started feeling warmer than usual. I had a temperature, and this persisted for a few days. It was clear that I should be taking this seriously. I had a brush with pneumonia a few years back and had heard somewhere that this could have had long term ramifications for my immune system and will have weakened my lungs to some degree.

I immediately, and voluntarily, decided to self-isolate. I waved goodbye to my family and went to a bedroom in the west wing of the Palace and began to rest. The only visitors I took were the royal physician and a house maid. The proper precautions were taken at all times – I insisted upon this, despite their protestations borne out of loyalty and a sense of duty. Communications were at a distance, and food, drink and medication placed on a trolley which was pushed across the floor with the assistance of a broom handle for the last couple of metres. The cutlery and plates were securely bagged up and simply disposed of, and the trolley sprayed with an antibacterial solution and thoroughly wiped down by a footman.

The first day or two was ok. I could read books and journals. Even watched a series on Netflix about some American red neck who ran a zoo full of Tigers. By now, I had a fever and something of a dry cough, but it was manageable and not too uncomfortable.

Many European countries and some US states had gone into an official state of lockdown. A means of legally enforcing – if necessary – that wherever possible, people are to remain in doors for a prolonged period; not interacting with other households. I had not done that. I didn't feel the need to be too repressive by imposing sanctions. I had no doubt that the people of our country are responsible enough to recognise the seriousness of the situation and act accordingly. We are adults. This is Monaco for goodness sake – not the UK!

It was after the first couple of days I became concerned. I had slipped into what can only be described as a feverish sleep. During the day, my body aches, hot flashes and chills had prevented me from resting peacefully. My fatigue eventually grew to the point where I could not do anything to remain conscious any longer. As I writhed around in my sweat soaked bed, my subconscious gave rise to a series of unusually vivid dreams; always switching between pleasant situations and disturbing ones.

One minute I would be dreaming of walking through a peaceful woodland in early Spring; coloured with the green shoots indicating an impending revival. It was warm, but crisp. I could still see my breath. The sun had begun to reveal itself through the clouds gearing up for its Summer residency in the sky. Bluebells and daffodils in full bloom all around me as the twigs cracked beneath my feet, having fallen to the ground from the trees above after a blustery Winter.

Then I would arrive at a nearby clearing in the woods, only to be greeted with melting stone statues of my children. I would look up to see that the clouds above my head were on fire, with deep purple plumes of smoke pouring up into the atmosphere, blotting out the sun. Reptile like creatures, wearing a chainmail of darkness, with oversized arms and legs scrabbled through the trees with the speed and movement of a Black Mamba snake reaching out, and trying to grab me, swiping at each of my limbs. Miraculously, I remained just out of their reach.

I have this feeling that I have lost something too. I'm not sure what. Did I have a bag with me? Or glasses? Or some kind of weapon to fend off these evil creatures? My attention is once again diverted elsewhere.

Behind the aggressive Mamba beasts, I can see a red glow in the distance. It quickly begins getting bigger and bigger. It is getting closer with every passing second, and as it gets closer, I can identify it as a lava ball. A giant lava ball. And as it gets progressively closer, I can begin to feel the heat. The heat grows more intense with every passing moment.

I'm still ducking and dodging the marauding limbs of the Mamba beast, but whilst originally feeling some relief that the giant lava ball would vanquish these enemies in hot pursuit of me, I now have a growing anxiety that unless I can also escape its path, this fiery sphere will also devour me. As the smoke from the raging flames in the clouds continue to make it ever darker, the bright red light emanating from the colossal lava ball counteracts this by shining brighter as it approaches.

I turn my back to the Mamba beasts for the first time, and run for my life, zigging and zagging to try and lose my pursuers. The heat grows ever more intense though, and I can hear the monsters are still on my tail. It hurts to breath in now. I can only breath in the hot air that is all around me. My throat is on fire. The giant lava ball has not devoured the Mamba beasts, hurling them into oblivion, instead it has politely remained just behind them, socially distancing itself, but also keeping pace with them, which means that they can all pursue me in unison.

There is a wall up ahead. I feel cripplingly hot and I cannot breathe anymore. And so, I awake.

With the images of my nightmare becoming too much for my unconscious brain to process, and the discomfort of the fever at an all-time high, I have come back to reality. I still cannot breathe efficiently. I need to shout for help, but I feel as though I only have the lung capacity to breath in 50-60% of the air that I actually need to be able to function. My heart is racing so I try and compose myself. On the table in front of me, there is a plastic glass full of water. I wonder where the trolley that usually stands there has gone and assume that it must be being cleaned somewhere.

As the panic lifts and I become capable of some degree of rational thought, I look around. I am not familiar with every room of the royal palace – having no need to go into most of them – but I definitely do not recognise this one. It is not like the bedroom I first retired to rest in. It is more like a small hospital room.

The room is about 5m x 5m, there is the bed I am laying on against one wall, a small table to my right and a single green faux-leather armchair to my left. There is nothing on the walls. At the foot of the bed, there is a small window – perhaps a foot wide – to allow for some ventilation. Although unbeknownst to me, I tell myself that it makes sense that we would have a suitable facility within the palace for any residents requiring medical attention. The priority once again becomes regulating my breathing, but not before I allow myself one more observation: unlike a regular hospital room, there is no medical equipment in sight.

Whilst I am more concerned with successfully breathing, the sense of alarm I am trying to control at being in these unfamiliar surroundings is not helping me regulate my heart rate or breathing. I manage to let out an audible groan for help. 'Doctor!'

The door is opened in an undramatic fashion. No particular urgency, or haste. A man in a typical set of turquoise hospital scrubs marches into the room. He is wearing a disposable face mask, and his hair is in a net. I am not sure if it is the effects of the fever, but I feel certain that he is not the palace Doctor who has been treating me. I don't know all the staff by name, nor do I sign off all their rotas, so I assume that there has been a shift change.

Without addressing me at all, he efficaciously looks at some notes in a file secured to the end of my bed and returns them within seconds. He leaves the room without any explanation.

The complete lack of due deference towards me I find puzzling, and I have never experienced it before.

He returns with what looks like a ventilator on a medical trolley. He wheels it across to my bedside and begins making it operational. Still not a word to me.

I ask him, where am I?

Pre-occupied with getting the equipment working as quickly as possible, "Same place you always are," comes the terse reply.

I ask him, how long have I been asleep.

He ignores this, continuing to wrestle with, and organise the leads and wires.

I ask him, what is this machine.

He ignores me again.

I ask, now between short breaths, where my press secretary is? I want to know what the public know.

This time he manages a sigh, but still does not answer any of my questions.

Angry, I attempt to reach out and grab his green gown to get his attention. Get him to stop what he is doing and to give me the respect of decent answer. The respect that anyone would expect, let alone a Head of State.

It is then that I notice for the first time, that both wrists are strapped to the bed. I look down; so are my ankles.

Whilst I lay there, in this state of bondage, I become more vociferous in my search for answers. Huskily screeching between panting breaths

I demand to know what is going on.

Not even an acknowledgement. But he does move a yard further back and continues his work from there.

I become more animated, and start thrashing around as much as the straps will allow me on the stained, sweat sodden, polyester bed sheets.

"How dare you ignore me!"

"Speak to me!" I rage

He pauses for a minute. And speaks.

"Calm down Mr Patton. Wait a moment, I'll be back."

Mr Patton? That explains it. There is a mistaken identity. Between the short breaths I manage a stifled chuckle.

"I'm not Mr Patton. I don't think my staff have informed you, if you just…"

By then the Doctor is retreating out of the room. "I'll be back in a moment, Sir."

"Don't go. You've made a mistake." I was feeling more anxious and agitated than ever.

"I demand you release me now!" I manage to shout as he places his gloved hand on the door handle to leave the room.

He hesitates, then returns to the bed once more and stoops down. Perhaps he has seen sense I think to myself.

But he was just picking something up. A newspaper. I caught sight of the headlines – the gist of which was the typical daily horror story analysis about the global pandemic we were caught up in. Next to an image I recognised as promoting an upcoming 'jungle based reality' show.

He straightens up, shakes his head, and folds it under his arm, turning around once more to leave.

"Where are you going?"

"Why won't you talk to me?"

Daylight floods through the door as it opens, and the Doctor exits through it.

"How dare you do this. I'M PRINCE FUCKING ALBERT."

Fear Is The Mind-Killer

Confucius say, "To see the right, and not to do it, is cowardice."

I feel like this. I can see the right, but I cannot bring myself to do it. I have several concerns.

I've been away from work for a while now. Almost 3 years in total. I've thought long and hard about when I knew something had changed in me and needed addressing. I wouldn't declare it as 'the start' of my problems, but there is an experience that sticks with me as being the moment that I realised something was not right. It was when I went to a music concert at an arena in Cardiff.

I've wanted to see The Corrs for years, ever since their landmark album came out in 1997: Talk On Corners. What an album. Spawned so many hits. The cover was split into 4 equal squares, each of which carried an individual picture of the four band members – all looking very attractive. Three sisters and one brother. If you didn't own it, you must have seen the CD case in Woolworths. Sold millions. In the charts for years?

They hadn't toured for ten years before this European trek. They had a year of dates, and then if they would ever play again together was very much a talking point. I couldn't miss this – and fortunately, my wife had bought us two tickets for my Christmas present.

The two of us went down. My daughter – although not interested anyway – was away at Uni as it was late January and term had just resumed after Christmas. Jenn was studying at the UCL – one of the top medical schools in the UK. She had worked very hard to get in, and spent several years highly focussed on her studies. She was in her third year and had decided to study Neuroscience. I guess I inspired her in more ways than one.

Although I didn't attend many concerts, football matches, nightclubs – basically any large, 'social spaces' – these days, I had dabbled as a younger man. As most younger people do to socialise. I wasn't a social butterfly, by any stretch – I was always too busy with my studies and practical work – but as part of university life of course I went out with some friends I had made. When we went our separate ways and on to our different routes in life, for the first few years we would meet up quite regularly. One of the guys would host, and we would all travel to their hometown or wherever their work had taken them and have a night out. A nice meal, sample some local wine bars and maybe a jazz club, for example. From maybe three or four a year, it's now maybe once every two or three years. The last one I went to was about five years ago. There's been one since, but I didn't go.

We took the train to the concert. I had a car, so it isn't something I needed to do as a rule, but I had no problem using public transport. Well trains, anyway, hate buses. Seems like they are constantly stopping every 300 yards; slowly plodding through the streets; jolting you about. I always seemed to end up next to someone who wanted to chat to me too. Not my bag that. Hadn't been on one in years.

Trains are quick and efficient, provided they were, a) punctual, and b) it isn't peak time. During this, the service almost resembles something you would see in a clickbait video depicting New Delhi railway station at rush hour. Too many people, not enough carriages. Standing room only, with everybody pressed up against each other. Hands feverishly gripping on to various yellow painted handrails – faded through years of sweaty residue. If this wasn't already a highly questionable practice, it would certainly need to be held to up to scrutiny after all of this.

It was a Tuesday evening, so the trains were fine, with plenty of places to sit. The ticket office was closed, so we waited for the on-board ticket inspector to purchase them from. He appeared through a door from the adjoining carriage within a few minutes of departure. Before the door closed shut behind him, I could see a gang of probably around a dozen males. Although mostly young, I would guess the age range went all the way up to 40. The noise they were making was what got my attention. It was a primitive, chest-beating aggressive chat utilising incessant – and unnecessary - expletives. And all of them swinging around either large cans or small liquor bottles, containing maybe gin, or vodka and a mixer, as they shouted back and forth. I remember remarking to my wife that I was glad we didn't sit there. I also remember feeling fairly tense for the rest of the journey. Luckily, I noticed that there was a toilet at the other end of the carriage, so they would not have to venture past us if nature called – which apparently it did, in some cases up to several times in about 30 minutes.

It was just a short walk to the arena from the train station. We were there a good couple of hours before showtime, and an hour before the doors even opened, but the queues to get in already circled around the building. We joined the queue, having previously had the ambition to enjoy a few pre-show drinks. Looked like that was going to be more difficult than we anticipated.

People continued to join the queue behind us at a steady rate. So much so that it seemed as though we were now in the middle of the line. Of course, this was before social distancing guidelines, but nonetheless, everyone seemed to be getting a bit closer than I was comfortable with. My wife was used to my limited patience in such a situation and sensed my growing annoyance at this lack of respect for personal space that everyone seemed to have.

The guy behind us jostled me a few times. There was nothing in it to be fair, but each time, I looked back at him with a knowing glance until he eventually acknowledged it with a 'sorry mate', when I accompanied the look with a loud sigh on the fourth or fifth occasion. Of course, paradoxically, not wanting any confrontation, I replied with a 'no problem' as though I had barely noticed.

My anxiety grew, when I saw a group of seven people conveniently 'meet up' with friends about 50 people ahead of us and just join them, forming a larger, more bulbous group within the line. All laughing, and generally looking pretty pleased with themselves. No regard for any of the hundreds of people standing in line behind them who had queued in an orderly fashion and in accordance with the protocols and etiquette of a polite society.

In my mind, when they did this, they had made a conscious and pre-meditated decision that their needs were more important than anyone else who stood in the line, and regardless of who it perturbed they were going to do as they pleased. Such narcissism made me livid. I felt the same when someone cut me up in the car, or when I walk past someone walking their dog and they allow it to jump all over you. "He won't hurt you" they cheerily tell you. "That's not the fucking point" was what I always wanted to tell them back.

So now, in my mind, this line had been thrown into chaos and until order was restored, I knew my heart rate would not slow down to normal nor my temper become less irritable. The line was two people wide almost all the way along, and now, 50 people ahead of me, it had this wider area where these individuals had barged in, exploding the line outwards. Like a cancerous growth, I thought to myself.

At the time I snapped at my wife when she tried to brush it off so we could continue our pleasant evening. I couldn't let it go, so told her that she was being stupid and that any reasonable person with a brain would be annoyed at these queue jumpers' antics. I later recognised that I was becoming far more agitated and tense, even by my standards. And sometimes it was when I had to deal with just the simplest of lifes problems. I know now that the only person that suffered for carrying around these negative thoughts was me.

When I was in this frame of mind, it became something of a downward spiral, and my mind would be become under siege from further intrusive worrying. It suddenly dawned on me what a perfect scenario this was to perpetrate a terrorist attack. A large group of contained people; limited exits; many even inebriated, perhaps impairing their ability to react appropriately – increasing the panic. Just a matter of months earlier, the Bataclan theatre in Paris was the scene of an ungodly and wicked mass shooting. American rock band, 'Eagles of Death Metal' were playing when 3 gunmen wearing suicide vests burst in shooting into the crowd. They killed 89 people that night and wounded around a further 200.

There was another shocking terrorism incident a year later: the unspeakably evil terrorist attack in Manchester at the Ariana Grande concert, where 22 innocent people died and 139 more injured. In fact, the first positive news I've heard during this lockdown has been that the brother of the suicide bomber had also been brought to justice for his part in the atrocity after being extradited from Libya. Of course, there is no justice on earth that can atone for the crime that he and his brother were responsible for. We were in an age where people were going to pop concerts to blow up little girls. It was no wonder I was experiencing these feelings lately, and felt that I could lose control at any moment. Surely every other person felt this way too?

Looking back, such thoughts seeped into every aspect of my life. Every time I went to the cinema, my decision of where to sit would be relative to the proximity of the emergency exits. As I went through the screen doors and turned the corner to survey the tiered seating, I would look where I could strategically sit to a) get out efficiently, and b) be furthest away so that I would not bear the brunt of the initial, pre-loaded magazine should a shooter storm in. I felt there would be little time to react initially, and changing the magazine could also offer precious additional seconds with which to act. This was assuming it was a single shooter – but I had reasoned that if there was more than one, they would probably take a different screen each to maximise impact. And, of course, it always had to be on the end of an aisle.

My wife must have seen I was drifting away, as she gave my hand a squeeze and said, 'come on'. I looked up to see the venue doors had opened and people were beginning to go into the building. Progress was slow as tickets were presented and checked, but also as handbags were searched and people were frisked as was the new norm.

We slowly shuffled to the front. A guy a few people in front of me had lit up a cigarette and began puffing away furiously before he reached the venue entrance. Now this bothered me too. I didn't know this man. Didn't know what he did for a living, whether he was a good guy, a bad guy. Didn't know if he'd fought in a war, or ever rescued kids from a burning orphanage. Didn't know if he volunteered in a charity shop, or if he ran homeless shelter food kitchens. All I knew was, he was smoking, and some of the smoke was blowing in my fucking direction. It was a selfish thing to do, he was guilty of it, and so I judged him on this one act alone.

And this is how my list of distresses would grow. I could never let anything go – especially in the moment. It was only when I was removed from a situation that things eventually stopped bothering me, and I was able to forget about things and move on.

We arrived at the front and we were greeted by the event security representative (a 'bouncer' still to me) on the door.

"Good evening Sir, Madam. Thank you for your company tonight, and we very much hope that you will have an enjoyable evening. If you could please show me your tickets, we will just complete security with you, and then I will point you to the direction of the cloakrooms are and you can proceed through."

He didn't say.

"Wait!" is what he did say, as he held up the palm of his hand, beckoning my wife forward with another one. A female security guard zipped across to silently complete security with her.

My wife was waved through, and then I was beckoned forward.

"Legs apart, empty your pockets."

Now I felt that I lived in the real world. I understand why we need to do this, and I also understand managing large groups of people is a difficult job and these guys have their work cut out. And believe me – I don't want to engage in friendly chatter in strangers either. But do I really need to be spoken to in the same way a criminal would be after he has just rocked up to the custody desk. Ive had experiences where this is not the case, so I know there are other alternatives if they can be bothered. As always, when I am sitting alone later tonight, I will spend the time thinking of a plethora of possible retorts that I could – and wished I had – given to him. He doesn't know who I am.

So, we were in. Swarms of crowds all moving in all possible directions. The merch stand was thirty deep. I wished I had had a few drinks to warm up. That takes the edge of my tension somewhat, but as I chase the feeling of the tension subsiding a little more with each drink, I can sometimes wind up in a different, but just as destructive place. I only really drank to relax. Or maybe forget, for a little while.

Finding the bar seemed a good idea. I announced the plan to my wife, and with some purpose to our direction, assertively cut our way through the people in the foyer. It was a 'floor - standing' type of gig. There was some balcony seating on the next level up which had a few rows of seats, but these were around the circumference of the inside area, and a little too far away from the stage to see what was going on. There were two bars – one on each side of the room. I could see as we entered the main hall, that both had queues of what seemed like a hundred people there already.

I needed a drink. My mouth had become strangely dry, and I had become really hot. I lead my wife across to the bar on the left and stood in another line. This one had partitions directing people where to stand. The ones that were made from that seat belt type material. It moved slowly – but our goal was near: a warm can of sub 4% lager poured into a plastic cup for our delectation. And all for a measly five quid.

We stood about a third back from the stage, making our drink last as long as possible to avoid the requirement to go back for more – and also to need the toilet, which was a similar situation. The Corrs had started. I had a rush of excitement at first, seeing them stroll on to the stage to their intro music. They all took a bow as I was giddily cheering.

"They're keeping all the crowd pleasers to the end," I remarked to my wife after about the eighth song into their setlist, having only recognised one album track so far. I tried to remain enthusiastic and offered up polite applause. For some people, including a man stood in front of me, the enthusiasm only grew with each passing track. I had clocked him getting drunker and drunker with a couple of friends over the course of the evening. He was old enough to know better, so I didn't think too much of it until during one song when he yanked his vest off, stood there bare chested and shouted out to the stage, "Oi Andrea [Corr], you can have a blow on my tin whistle if you like" before proceeding to roll up laughing – sloshing beer all over the place as he did. Some went on my wife.

"Watch it," I told him. He turned around, told me to chill out and carried on with his raucous behaviour. I suggested we move, but my wife – probably fearing I'd find fault wherever we stood – said we were fine where we were. A few upbeat numbers came on, and he began dancing around too. A little more beer was sloshed around, a few elbows bumped us, shoes stood on. I ignored it for a few minutes, until I tapped him on the shoulder and asked him to watch what he was doing. This time, he simply told me to "fuck off."

The pressure of having to act decisively dawned on me. What should I do? He cannot speak to me like that in front of my wife. I made a reasonable request. We are all trying to enjoy ourselves. I cannot let this go; I need to act. What should I do? Should I fight him? Would I be a coward for not starting a fight, or would it be worse to fight for fear of being called a coward for not fighting? The meaning of what constitutes a coward these days had baffled me. Would it now be a dereliction of duty to not punch this man?

I was becoming more aware of a hot flush I was having, and I put it down to a result of this burgeoning confrontation. The live music now sounded distant, as all I could hear in my head was this conversation with myself. I never really got headaches, but I had one now. And I suddenly felt as though I had a tight band across my chest area. My breathing became more laboured, and beads of perspiration appeared on my brow. I could tell from the look of concern on my wife's face that I should be worried.

She started leading me away by the hand, out of the crowd. The increasing gravity of the situation had allowed me to park my dispute for a moment as my 'fight or flight' instinct kicked in. Not only couldn't I breath, but now my legs were beginning to feel like jelly, and I was trembling. As I walked through the crowd to the back of the hall, all I can remember is just wading through a sea of faces in near darkness. It seemed endless, and I felt scared that I would never get out. The look in each persons eye every time they saw me coming through. It was a look of pity, but also a strange blend of disdain and discomfort. I didn't understand.

I reached the back, found a wall to lean on and slumped down to the ground. My limbs were tingling, I couldn't breath and my chest pain was growing. My wife was now shouting for assistance. One of the nearby event security personnel responded rapidly and put out a call on his radio for some more help. I was sure I was having a heart attack, and I felt sure my time was up. It was an intense rush of symptoms I had never felt before. Two of the event security had helped me to my feet and assisted me out of the hall. I remember my wife having tears running down her face and following behind, as Andrea Corr belted out 'I never really loved you anyway' behind us. Bugger – I missed my favourite song.

Around 3 hours later we arrived back home. The venue had called an ambulance, and on the basis, it was a suspected cardiac issue, they had prioritised the call and arrived in about 15 minutes. However, as they arrived, I had begun to feel marginally better. The ambulance took me in to the hospital anyway, and I had an ECG (which was clear). The long and the short of it was, I'd had a severe panic attack. And it had turned out to be the first of many that I was going to have in the next six months.

I had always struggled with anxiety, but I now recognise it to be something referred to as high functioning anxiety. This is not a medically accepted condition (at the moment), but I feel that the principal of it applies to me and can relate to it. It refers to people who live with anxiety, but who are able to function well in most aspects of their life. In fact, it is when the anxiety propels you forward rather than leaving you frozen in fear. Any type of anxiety is actually linked to the primitive instincts our ancestors had; its roots are in threat awareness and detection, for instance. On the surface, I appeared successful, calm and together. But this isn't how I felt inside.

Beneath the sharp suits and exceptional punctuality, I was a ball of nervous energy, fretting about every detail, afraid of failure and of disappointing others. I wasn't sleeping, had a racing mind, and a complete inability to 'enjoy the moment'. It was always tainted by expecting the worst to follow. I compared myself to others and developed a mental fatigue. And when you don't recognise it, it's so easy to disregard it, and say, "it's because I'm a workaholic", "it's because I'm competitive", "it's because I'm a perfectionist."

I have had lots of time to think about lots of seemingly innocuous things that I have experienced over the year, and the sum total paints a different picture to how I saw it when I was living it. I've reflected on things my loved ones, mainly my wife, have pointed out to me over the years. Things I dismissed without giving any credit to. And that's because I felt I was successful, and that my actions had brought about a positive life for my family – so why would I listen to anyone else's opinion? The outcomes were positively reinforcing my course of action.

But things built up. I talked about this one particular incident, not because it ended up with a trip to A and E and unexpectedly ended up being my last day at work for the next three years, but because I can now see that it a cocktail of triggers were in place on this night that brought me down. And it emotionally overloaded me.

My overriding fear of a large space with a lot of people;
The noisy lads drinking on the train;
The queue outside the venue;
Being jostled in the queue;
Queue jumpers;
Fear of a terrorist attack;
A smoker in the line;
The curt event security (who ended up doing a fantastic job of looking after me);
The disorder inside the venue;
Cannot get a drink quickly enough;

The drunken dickhead in the crowd (it was ok to judge this guy).

And that's before some more minor things that I got hung up on too – such as mentally debating using public transport in the first place or drinking from plastic cups. I'm learning that this stuff isn't worth your energy. The guy selling you the lager doesn't sweat it for a second. The person manufacturing the plastic glass isn't worried. The Managing Director of the arena will only care when people stop buying it – and there is no suggestion of that ever happening. Nobody cares, and nothing will change that. I am working on letting it go too.

The only treatment I can subscribe to for this is psychological therapies, talking therapies. Cognitive Behavioural Therapy (CBT) is the best treatment in my opinion and has helped me get this under control. It has taught me to think and behave in a different way to manage my problems. My negative thoughts and feelings were trapping me in a vicious cycle and I eventually became overwhelmed.

I meet my therapist twice a week, and its helped. However, I have crystallised some of my fears and I am struggling with them as I still feel they are steeped in a logical rationale.

I am not good on public transport. I do not like visiting shopping centres. And more broadly speaking, I do not like leaving my home.

I'm still edgy and alert. I still feel like I'm losing control. Sometimes, when I do go out – maybe for a walk to the local shop and back – I feel like people are looking at me and somehow observing my anxiety. Even with everything going on in the world, when I go on my daily government endorsed walk, I still feel this way. I know it is ridiculous. If anything, they are probably doing their best to avoid contact with anyone else altogether! But it's just a feeling I find hard to shake, even though I've had a word with myself.

I live by myself now, which is fine. My wife found it too difficult to cope with me at home all the time scrutinising her and making her on edge. Thank God it happened before this lockdown! I bet she's high fiving herself now. We still talk, and she is still currently my wife, though this is just in name only. She moved into a nice apartment on the waterfront in Cardiff. She volunteered to move. She knew it would be a potential issue for me, and she wanted a fresh start. We are on good terms, she still calls to check on me, but I think she can finally relax now. Jenn is working for the Royal Berkshire NHS Trust now and living in Reading having graduated from the UCL. She discretely filmed her graduation for me from a clip-on camera and whatsapp'd it to me after. I was so proud.

I want to make her proud too. But I am not sure if I can do it.

I have had three long years to try and get back on track, and I have made progress, albeit has been slow. I've spoken to my Management team and trade union representative many times and they have, overall, been very supportive. I was getting close to a return to work 'naturally', I was sure of it. I have been offered further support to ease my way back in, such as flexible hours, 'time out' sessions and a phased return.

Although I am sure returning to work will be a positive step, I am frightened of rushing it. I am concerned about the setback that could bring with it. But again, I am concerned that I will be in dereliction of duty if I do not. Again, my mind is occupied with the notion of cowardice and what it means. My understanding was always of cowardice was in the traditional, often military, sense of the word. I've always had an interest in history, and as I had a lot of time on my hands to read and consume more in the last few years, these historical figures seemed to resonate with me.

US General James H Ledlie. Upon being given command of Union troops during the "Battle of the Crater" in the U.S. Civil War, he sent his troops into an extremely dangerous situation, whilst he stayed back in a bunker drinking rum. The military effort was a disaster and he was dismissed from service.

General Horatio Gates, born in Maldon, Essex. Famous for fleeing the Battle of Camden and riding a respectable 270km in three days to safety.

Or, if I really wanted to give myself a hard time, Saddam Hussein. The man who sent thousands of men into battle across three wars, but when faced with death himself, surrendered to save his own skin.

These were traditional interpretations of cowardice to me, but perhaps it's meaning is more elusive now?

This does not mask the fact, however, that there is a crisis in this country at present, and I have some specialist skills that are no doubt required. A Respiratory Consultant Physician could make a valuable contribution to the national effort, and I need to step up. They are advertising regularly on TV for medical professionals to return to work – whether that meant returning from retirement, or from a career change. Emotive words and phrases are deliberately used like, 'Step Up' and 'Be a Hero' to entice you back in. And of course, they are right to do so. They are heroes.

I am not afraid of a virus – at all. That is not to say I am immune, it's just having been surrounded by such threats for years, you develop a whole different perspective. In my gap year, I worked in villages in Botswana where 1 in 4 adults was infected with AIDS. I am not afraid of that.

But I **am** afraid of leaving the house. I am afraid of losing control and how that could let people down.

So, I sit here alone in my house, day after day, endlessly watching the news. Wasting my abilities, and my training. Hearing about how everyone in the NHS is a hero. Everyone except me.

I can't bear Thursdays when people gather on their doorsteps clapping.

You can hear it all around the estate. I go and take a shower at exactly 7:58pm, so I cannot hear any of it.

I cannot bear it. It makes me feel useless.

Like a broken robot.

I am a coward.

Gifts Never Given

The alarm had already been deactivated, I realised, as I unlocked the side entrance door and walked into the building. The alarm control panel was next to this access point. If you had instead opted to unlock the building and enter through the main showroom entrance, you would have to make an undetected forty-foot sprint across to the alarm panel to disarm it. Whilst a fun challenge, it was near impossible, and you would almost certainly set the alarm off. So, there could either be someone here already, or it wasn't set properly the last time someone locked up.

It couldn't be the latter, as the last person to leave the showroom – as far as I could be aware – was me. I had been setting that alarm for over ten years, and my approach was highly methodical, every time I left the building. I would complete a check of all the internal doors to check that that they were firmly closed. This would prevent a sensor picking them up and declaring them as 'open', in turn, setting off the alarm. Once the code was punched into the alarm panel, it gave you thirty seconds to get out of the building, and to secure the door. Realistically, this took no more than ten seconds, so the final part of my procedure would be to wait for the full thirty seconds to elapse and then I could be sure it was set correctly. One final check that the door was secure, and it was done. No – that couldn't be the reason. I had never taken short cuts with this.

Perhaps our vehicle technician – in to deal with emergency key worker's vehicles - had arrived before me.

I locked the door behind me as I came in and went into the showroom area. Our car showroom had recently been modernised, so despite the building being over thirty years old, the internal finishing's were of a very high standard. It was a medium sized dealership, which fit up to 14 display cars inside at a squeeze. On site, there was also a workshop area (for mechanical repairs etc) and the parts stores. Outside there was also a used car display area that comfortably housed exactly 44 vehicles. In the ten years plus, I had been managing the business, we'd had a very successful run. This made it even more eerie when I had been attending the site these last few weeks.

The usual hustle bustle had been replaced with silence. No customers coming and going. No staff running between offices, collecting things from the printer or looking for a set of keys. No familiar whirr of the coffee machine making one of its many cups of coffee per day.

Gone was the rush of excitement from amongst the team when a song came on the showroom radio that they recognised - punctuating the otherwise drab, background, elevator music that endlessly played.

At 10.30am, there would be no honking of the horn as the sandwich man pulled up in the car park. This was usually accompanied by a stampede of around half of the staff in the business, as they rushed outside to buy overpriced food - like it was a precious commodity, or that they hadn't eaten in days.

I would even miss the annoying things I had to ensure - like endlessly reminding the team to check the customer toilets for cleanliness and replace the toilet roll where necessary. No need now – the current roll had lasted for weeks, and still had half the sheets remaining on it.

The printer never ran out of paper either. And the fridge no longer needed restocking. Even the plastic red dog bowl in the front foyer no longer needed topping up with water.

I looked over and made my usual observations in the showroom (no signs of any security or maintenance issues) and went over to my office. There was a multitude of showroom spotlights which took a short while to warm up and fully illuminate, so I never bothered putting those on. I also thought that if people saw lights on from outside, they could presume we were open in some way, and try to gain access. Or even the police would stop by and make some enquiries as to what I was doing in the building during lockdown. Car sales showrooms were on the government's list of non-essential businesses, quite clearly, in black and white. I turned my office light on and set up my laptop.

We were five weeks into the lockdown now, and I had been attending the site a minimum of two, sometimes three, days a week. Everyone else, apart from one 'on call' technician, had been furloughed. So, it was down to me to respond to customer communications, check site security, and some other things that I couldn't do from my study at home. Every Thursday was when we tended to have our weekly company Zoom meetings, with Managers and Directors alike in attendance. Last week, we had debated opening the aftersales side of the business in two weeks' time. It had seemed as though we had every justification for doing so, and it had looked likely. I hadn't heard anything further since then, however, from anyone.

I preferred to take the conference call on site if I could co-ordinate my visit to coincide with the time. One reason was that it was easier, in the sense that there was no chance of being disturbed by one of the kids. The other reason was that I just think it looked better, and demonstrated I was more engaged with the business and being pro-active.

I have two girls, twelve and six, and whilst they are beautifully behaved – and are working very hard with their Mother on their home schooling – it is inevitable to expect some background noise, or occasional commotion. Equally, I didn't particularly want them to overhear the content of one of our meetings either. They could sometimes get quite 'animated'.

My Wife and girls had gone into lockdown a week earlier than me, when the schools had closed, and since this they had not been anywhere. I was grateful that my week could at least be broken up by trips into the business. Aside from their daily dog walk – she only had little legs, so it was never a long walk – they had not ventured further than the back garden.

I reflected on this for a moment. That was a long time for them to be physically cut off from their friends and extended family. It must be very confusing for them at that age – being taken away from all these significant people in their life. I was passionate about ensuring their day was structured and that they were being productive, with plenty of schoolwork being completed. I decided I would have a chat with my Wife tonight when I got home about easing up on them and spending more time checking that they were ok.

My Wife had also been doing an amazing job of trying to juggle working full time from home and manage the kids' lessons. Her job in customer service meant that she was taking phone calls on and off all day. The kids had to work through the lesson plans the school had set, largely wearing headphones to block out the talking. But despite this, she managed to monitor the two girls progress, assist and explain when required, provide and serve lunch, and get through a mountain of customers' calls on a daily basis. I must remember to tell her what a great job she was doing and thank her.

I scanned through my emails. I hadn't had any since last Thursday, which was odd. The first few weeks I bombarded with questions from people. They could generally be sorted out into two baskets as well. The first type of query was along the lines of, 'I have something booked on (XX date in the future) – will I need to rebook', and the second type of quote was related to how they could get a payment break on their car payment. It had all happened so suddenly; despite our best attempts we couldn't contact every customer personally to tell them we had closed. Also, we didn't know how long this was going on for, so we had dealt with the immediate bookings first. We eventually caught up to date and stayed on top of it, so it made sense that the emails had dried up somewhat.

Emails from people enquiring about purchasing a car were very few and far between anyway, so their absence didn't surprise me. The only other type of email I had been receiving were the usual daily automated emails. The online delivery calendar, the telephone call stats, that kind of thing.

With nothing to report, it made sense that they were temporarily suspended too.

I leaned back in my ergonomically sound desk chair, and said out loud to myself, "So no meetings, no emails. Let's go and see Jack in the workshop." The workshop and parts department took up the entire back half of the building, so effectively ran the same length of the showroom, behind my office. I got up and walked through the middle office (nobody used this office space – there was too much thoroughfare for anyone to concentrate) which took you out into the workshop area.

Jack was the technician who had almost pleaded to be able to carry on working – he would be in every day if he could. In accordance with the government advice, and in the interest of looking after staff, we just retained his services for working on key workers' cars. As far as the rest of the team went, we had decided to close the workshop – despite it being somewhat a grey area as to whether it could be kept open under the umbrella of an 'essential service'.

I could see that he must be running out of work to do, as the floor was still wet from being thoroughly mopped. He was stood across the far side in one of the vehicle bays. A vehicle was up in the air on his ramp, and he was using a high torque wheel nut remover on the wheels. He must have had a problematic nut on one of the wheels as it seemed to be taking far longer than it should. These guns were making quite a racket, which reverberated and echoed around the otherwise empty workshop. To compound this, he had music playing loudly from his work bench.

I called across to him, "Morning mate," but he could not have heard me over the noise of the gun. I waited for a break in his activities, and called over once more, but I noticed that in addition to the noise he was (wisely) wearing ear defenders, rendering my efforts to get his attention pretty futile. I waved my arms around, but he was looking the other way Rather than potentially slipping and breaking something on the wet floor tiles, I decided to return to my office and catch up with him later.

I walked back through to the showroom side of the building. With all the spotlights off, and just relying on the natural light, it was dimly lit. Between that and the lack of people and music, it always made me get a sense of incredible loneliness. It wasn't just that – I've been in the showroom alone many times, out of hours. It was the lack of cars passing on the road outside, and the vacant car parks of all the nearby businesses that polarised it.

I sat back down in my desk chair. I had already put up the new signage ready for when we re-open, last week. I had tidied up and emptied all the office bins way back in week one. I had even been out in the vehicle compound cleaning all the bird shit off the cars several times in the last few weeks. 'Let's have a quick read of the headlines,' I said to myself.

I logged on to the BBC website and loaded the news homepage. As usual these last couple of months, the vast majority of the headlines were dedicated to providing the latest stats from the pandemic, at home and abroad. Deaths had now risen to over 20,000 in the UK. That was just reported deaths in hospitals – it stood to reason there were many more than this. The same went for reported cases. There must have been thousands more. Some cases were probably mild and so the NHS were never contacted, and some people probably contracted the virus but had written it off as the flu before anyone was properly aware of its identity.

There were a couple of non-virus stories (one covering a legal challenge from the USA women's soccer team for equal pay), then below this was an article entitled 'When will we have a vaccine?' I clicked on it and read how whilst typically it could take years or even decades to develop a vaccine, with a huge collaborative effort, scientists were aiming to achieve this in a matter of months. Human trials were already being undertaken.

I scrolled down the page and idly looked through the comments on the message board at the bottom. It documented a mixture of public feelings on the article, which generally ranged from people asserting that such a thing would be 'impossible', through to the many bashing the government for their alleged initial inaction on the matter.

It was all pretty samey, and I was about to look for another article, but one particular post caught my eye. Amidst the ranters and the usual know-it-all's holding court, there was a post which was incongruous with the heated conversation.

The author of the post opened the plea, "Can somebody please tell me what I am supposed to do." It went on to say how he – or she, it was never clarified – was over the age of 70 years old, has had a heart attack and currently had blood cancer. This level of immunity concerns would have placed them well and truly in the most vulnerable persons category, whom the government would have contacted to tell to remain in isolation at home for a 12-week period.

He claimed to have had been told that is he had symptoms to not contact a pharmacy, GP or hospital, but to stay at home for seven days. I had to assume that he did have symptoms, but equally he either needed critically important medication or the attention of a Doctor. I wondered who had given him this advice, and whether it was the correct advice to follow. But it was the final couple of lines that hit me hard:

"After 7 days, if I'm still alive, am I then allowed to ask for help? Please advise because I am terrified."

In the middle of many of the ensuing message board battles on this page, with verbal bows and arrows being fired back and forth between participants – being sure to reference the post number each time, that they were responding to – in the middle of the battlefield, the no mans land, you had this vulnerable individual begging for some help. And instead of a response, the post was ignored, and the battles raged on around him instead; everyone immersed in their own little pointless feud. I was disgusted to the core by the lot of them.

What made it poignant to me was that the comment was dated 24th March 2020. That was more than four weeks ago. My heart sank, and the only thing I could think of was to wonder whether he was still alive. Did he get the help he needed? Did someone eventually reach out to him to assist him in his hour of need? The post suggested to me he did not have anyone else to turn to.

I felt helpless – there was nothing I could do. There was no way of identifying the person from the post. If I went on and added a comment now four weeks after the event, it would not be noticed – even if it was not too late. I could not get this howl of pain from the past out of my mind.

I contemplated contacting the website division of the BBC to try and task them to find out. Should they accept responsibility for the persons welfare? They will be the only ones privy to the users identity, after all. Would total inaction not give them some culpability? I do not expect them to tend to the welfare of all their users, but this post wreaked of desperation from a seemingly defenceless, elderly individual. The details they had for this person could surely have been passed along to an appropriate agency. Or did the risk of a GDPR breach and the subsequent fines that could be imposed upon them scotch any such compassionate thinking? Isn't modern life great.

My attention was drawn as I saw Jack go past my office. He was talking on his mobile phone with somebody. From the gist of the conversation it seemed as though he was expecting a vehicle to be recovered into our compound. From what I could glean, it sounded as though the car had been involved in a very serious road traffic accident.

I got up and stood in my office doorway to earwig the call, trying and pick up a bit more detail. From what I could gather the vehicle had been involved in a head on collision with a car carrying a group of teenagers. The fire service had cut the roof of the car we were expecting in, and having conducted their investigation, now needed the car to be stored until the insurance paperwork had been completed. I was certain I overheard Jack mention that this incident had a fatality too. Strange it had been brought to us, as we did not have a Bodyshop, but I figured we must have supplied it.

During this lockdown I had noticed that there was a huge increase in the amount of irresponsible driving I had witnessed on the roads. It seemed as though people were taking advantage of the huge reduction of traffic that was on the roads – as well as the police service being somewhat pre-occupied at the moment – to drive around at high speeds, cutting across lanes on a whim and driving extremely aggressively in general.

With his phone still pressed against his ear, Jack went outside to open the gates in readiness for the recovery lorry's imminent arrival. I sat back down and went back to my news headlines. I clicked the link for local news to see if I could find anything about this road accident.

When I left home this morning, the girls were about to start their 30-minute PE lesson conducted by an affable young chap from Essex. My youngest was more enthusiastic about it, whilst my eldest, less so. They did it a couple of times a week to make sure they were staying active. It probably gave my Wife half an hour respite too. I was looking forward to going home. Since lockdown began, we had spent most of our waking moments together, and the bonding we had done was priceless. They told me that they hated it when I left the house to come into work and counted down the minutes my return.

I wouldn't stay too long today – there was precious little point in doing so anyway. On the way home I would visit the supermarket and stock up for the next four or five days. It's incredible how quickly you go from a full fridge to an empty fridge when everybody is at home 100% of the time. I was hoping that they would still have some Easter eggs left that they were selling off very cheaply. If so, I would grab the girls one each.

They had been doing so well with their home schooling and interacting together beautifully. I think I'll pick up the ingredients to make their favourite too – a home-made Nandos dinner! I had planned to buy all three of them a present – something awesome – to mark when the lockdown was eased. Kind of a reward for seeing it through with such wonderful attitudes. I wasn't sure what my eldest would like, but my youngest needed a new TV/DVD combi for her bedroom, and my wife needed a new handbag. I'll start looking maybe this afternoon – no expense spared (within reason).

Glancing over the local news headlines, they mirrored the national headlines. All pandemic related and lots of statistics, broken down by each local council territory. I remembered that it was last week the incident happened, so I continued scrolling down - looking through progressively older news as I did. I could hear the breakdown lorry arriving outside in the car park.

There it was. Dated last Thursday. The headline was bleak: "CRASH LEAVES TWO DEAD, THREE FIGHTING FOR THEIR LIFE." It was on the dual carriageway about 3 miles from my house – I don't know how this managed to escape my attention. Selecting the story and scanning through it, the accident involved two cars colliding at speed where a slip road intersected on to the dual carriageway. One car, with four young men, had been going in excess of 100 miles per hour – cameras had observed them changing lanes without warning and behaving generally erratically – and the other car, with a single male occupant, was joining the dual carriageway. Both drivers had perished, and all the passengers contained in one of the cars were in intensive care.

It had a picture of both cars. One was a Golf Gti – boy racers wet dream – and the other car…well the other car was the same car that I drove. In the same colour. The unusual aspect of that was it was a recently launched colour in the range. We had only received a delivery of one of these units so far - which the one I was driving. It must have been sourced from another dealer.

I could hear voices outside. It was Jack talking to the recovery driver. I walked over to the large showroom windows. Sure enough, it was the same car as mine. Jack and the driver were not engaging in the usual chatty banter I would have expected. Few words appeared to being exchanged. In fact, Jack was several metres away from the driver, sat on the kerb with his head in his hands. He was shaking his head slowly from side to side every few seconds. I knocked the window to get his attention. I wanted to see if he was ok. Neither man turned at first, so I hit the window harder. Still nothing.

I hit the window still harder. And harder. And harder.

Nobody flinched.

I moved towards the doors to go outside and speak to them, but I couldn't open then. Jack must have locked them when he went outside? I rattled the door, but no one looked up. But from this angle, I had a different perspective on the damaged car.

I know that reg number.

Heart racing, I ran back to my office to read the news report more thoroughly. It can't be.

I heard the external door opening, and Jack coming back towards my office. I shot up when he appeared in the doorway.

"JACK! What is going on – who's car is that?"

He stared at my seat and wiped his eyes – stifling an apparent urge to start sobbing.

"JACK – SPEAK TO ME."

He continued to stare. Right through me.

"JACK…"

He gave a huge sigh, wiped his eyes, turned off my office light, and left the room. Gently closing the door behind him.

Stripy Jumper

I first clapped eyes on him while passing through his garden sometime in late April. My work at home was completed, and I was now finally able to go out into the big wide world to work. It couldn't have come soon enough, especially as I was only too aware that I was probably in the last few weeks of my life.

I had worked hard right from the start. Even when I was very young, I was given lots of responsibilities. My first role was to nurture and help with the babies. Most friends my age started out this way too. Collectively we would prepare all their meals from scratch - processing all the incoming raw materials brought to us. Then when it was ready, we would feed it to them. It was hard, but necessary work to ensure our community was able to thrive and survive. My role eventually evolved into preparing meals for 'Her Royal Highness' too!

After a little while of doing this, I went on to a couple of short stints with the internal construction team and security office. It broadened my skill base, but I knew what I wanted to do long term.

Overall, I had been happy with the jobs I was allotted. Especially as the alternative was to be on 'mortuary duty'. This meant that my responsibilities would have been to remove the dead carcasses of both the elderly and the babies that didn't survive. They would need to be taken far away from our commune to reduce the likelihood of any diseases taking hold and spreading within. It was a truly horrifying job, even though you got to get out and explore a bit.

Once I was old enough to leave, the word came back – I had been selected. I was ecstatic. My new duty meant that I would be able to leave home, and collect the resources we needed myself, bringing them back for my replacement to prepare and serve instead. I could not wait to travel and see the bright colours of the world. There was no doubt that my new job would be super dangerous and extremely tiring, but it was all so liberating. I was so excited.

This duty meant that I would be expected to work from the time the sun came up until sunset - with no real breaks in between, but I didn't care. It was the best job in society as far as I was concerned. The job was so much better in the Summer too. The role was a totally different proposition in Winter, and whilst it had higher mortality rates it was very boring as you didn't get to go anywhere. Essentially you were responsible for helping preserve the supplies with some additional security and core monitoring duties. It was of course a very important job, and I was thankful for their efforts as it provided me with this future opportunity, but all the same I felt lucky that I would not be around to suffer that.

It was whilst I was foraging one day that the shuffling, slightly hunched figure caught my eye. I regularly passed a garden in Marston Moretaine on my usual way to work. It was about a mile away from a churchyard that we were living near at the time. There was not an abundance of flowering plants present in this garden, it had been mainly landscaped with stones and some evergreen perennials, but there was a particularly tall honeysuckle plant. It was at least three metres high, and clearly very mature. Floods of its bright pink, trumpet shaped fragrant flowers cascaded from the top to almost the very bottom. Looking at it, I could almost taste the sweet nectar held within.

I had always intended to venture in one day to take a closer look but had not gotten around to it as yet. As I looked across today, I could see that there was some level of activity going on, and it all seemed to be centred around a very slow-moving man. He was clearly the centre of attention, but he was not on his own in his front garden. There were several other people present, facing him, albeit standing a small distance back from him. As he advanced forward, they would advance backwards. Some of them were also carrying some kind of tools with them. One man had his eye pressed against a plastic tube connected to a black box with a long tail, that sat atop a three-legged tree. Another man wielded a long stick with what looked like a furry dead rat on the end of it. The woman was the only one talking and stood very elegantly whilst speaking into some kind of portable tube.

There were some other people too, including several men who lined his driveway – standing still like statues. They all had matching outfits and hats on. Just outside the garden, the road was full of cars and vans. Some of the vans had large white dishes stuck to the top, with a stick pointing up to the sky.

I was a little early for work, and at this time of year the stock resource was so bountiful that I knew I could catch up anyway, so I decided to go across to see what was going on. Without disturbing anyone, I sidled over and sat on a small wooden gate to observe. From here, I could better see the main attraction.

The man was clearly very old. Despite the unseasonably warm weather, he wore a dark suit jacket with large gold buttons, which would sparkle when the sun caught them as he shuffled forward. The sun would also sparkle on what appeared to be three large coins attached to the front of his jacket – two in the shapes of stars. He wore a suit and tie and whilst in deep concentration, he frequently glanced up to smile at those observing him.

He would creep from one end of the driveway area to the other and then back again. Everyone else kept quiet whilst patiently watching. I wondered how old he must be. I knew that I was just weeks away from the end, and I hoped that I would be so graceful and dignified when my speed and steadiness has become impeded.

As I sat and watched for a few minutes, my attention was drawn back to the honeysuckle beyond the pacing gent. The flowers were in full bloom, nurtured by a loving mother nature. Teeming in its tenacious buds that have multiplied in a similar way to the most ferocious cells in the blood, I felt even more drawn than before to this small urban meadow. Perhaps today would be the day I investigate and maybe capture some of its treasures and put them in my back pockets to take home.

I leapt up to make my way through the crowd and to make it over to the plant. I tried to keep out of the way of everyone.

As I first breached the yard, I immediately became involved in an altercation with the young attractive woman, holding her pipe object. I had not meant to disturb her, but there was a smell wafting from her that I could not ignore. It was a sweet, flowery scent that had distracted me and grabbed my attention. In a trance and running solely on instinct, I had wavered from my path, unconsciously curious.

My sudden presence alarmed the young woman, who immediately shrieked and began waving her arms around. The scene was formerly so serene and friendly, that the abrupt influx of noise and gesticulations took me somewhat aback. Startled, I veered backwards to avoid the woman's swiping hands from catching me. There was an intense but incoherent distress from this woman and I just wanted to shut her and her glassy, rasping squeals up.

I sensed that I was now the prime reason for a real raucous sight, and I didn't like the people staring. Particularly while the old gent was being revered so, in this albeit unexplainable ceremony.

I acted upon impulse and in a panic. I had felt threatened and I wanted the fuss to end immediately.

I followed the source of the carbon dioxide I could detect and went in for the kill.

It was just a reaction, and the wrong one.

Now I lay here on the cobbles, waiting until my lights go out for good. I would not see any more of this summer, or any season.

My barbed stinger had become lodged in her skin. I had known there was a high chance of this happening were I to sting something as tough as human skin. This had meant my stinger had ripped off and was now left in the lady's arm. As I disconnected, I could feel that my stinger had been torn loose from my abdomen and knew that this process had therefore ripped out my internal organs. It would be a maximum of a few minutes before I died.

I looked across the garden for one final time. The man appeared to have found a renewed sense of determination and drive as he completed what transpired as being one final lap with much aplomb, and then stopped. There was some polite applause as somebody wasted no time in thrusting a long black pole with an orange on the end under his nose which the old gent began to talk into.

I listened to his wise, gentle voice carrying across the garden - hoping it would be the one that sang me to sleep.

Dispute Conjugale

The cunt had sat there doing nothing all day.

It was a sunny day, not too hot, maybe 20-ish degrees. We had got the barbeque out, put on some burgers and sausages; nothing too remarkable because it was all that we had in. It was a gas barbeque – albeit, an old wobbly one – so it was a case of turning on the gas and pushing the meat around on the grill now and again. Then when it was ready, putting it between the two buns and adding on a slice of cheese. A fucking idiot could do it.

A fucking idiot did do it.

Apart from that, the useless cunt had done nothing.

The kids had nagged to play a board game, so they all sat down and did that for an hour. It was some kind of card game. Our youngest, Elena, who was 7, won. She had let the whole neighbourhood know about it too with her noisy celebrations, done deliberately just to wind her older sister up who suspected that she had been shown some leniency in order to be victorious. I had told them to keep it down; they were being too noisy. They all soon shut up.

When I played games with them, I insisted on equality regardless of the factor that her sister, Lola, 11, was older. When I didn't play, she was given free rein to basically cheat. I was told that it was because she was younger, and to give her a chance. I don't think they get anything out of that approach – except teaching a child to become lazy and selfish. To throw a tantrum if things don't go their way. It winds me up, and if my buttons are pressed anymore then, after all this, I am seriously considering seeing to it so that they don't get the chance to play games together so much anymore. Maybe at all – depends how I am feeling.

After this they'd taken the dog for a walk to enjoy their government permitted daily exercise. It was a short walk, a couple of kilometres. Only took half an hour or so. There was no one about, until you got to the lake, and then there were several other families with the same idea normally. I didn't go today. I was fed up with bumping into (figuratively speaking – we all kept our distance of two metres) the same faces and having the same conversation.

"Oh hi XXX….yes we are indeed out walking our dog again…..we haven't been doing anything really….yes I did hear the latest death toll….terrible isn't it…..it's such a scary/weird situation isn't it…..just waiting for the grass to grow so I can mow it again…..are you staying in or staying in tonight lol……the boredom is driving me mad…..looking forward to go back to work….but you should know all this…because it's all THE SAME FUCKING STUFF WE TALKED ABOUT YESTERDAY."

Sometimes, I just cannot be bothered with it – and one day last week was one of those days. I didn't have the energy to keep up the façade that was required in the event I ran into one of the 'professional mothers' from the school, as I called their clique. I didn't want to risk having to be forced into having to have a public conversation, either, with that loser. Smiling and hiding behind a thin veneer that shielded everyone from the truth. I was able do it, it just riled me more. It would be worse actually meeting someone I hadn't bumped into recently, as I seriously doubted my ability to follow the usual conversation blueprint for the 'first' time with any level of enthusiasm. I wondered if people who have these pointless conversations enjoy having them.

For me, a conversation should have some direction, a purpose. I can't just 'say words' for the sake of saying words. This is another aspect of lockdown that intensely annoys me – forced chit chat. For example, someone saying to me – in a patently hot, Summers day where the temperature is high – 'it's lovely today isn't it.' As an initial observation this is fine. For example, making this remark when you first arrive in the garden on such a day, is a valid expression of how the actual weather exceeds your original perception of how nice a day you thought it was. Sitting there for several hours with another person, and in lieu of having a meaningful conversation, just coming out with, 'nice day isn't it,' for me, is a waste of time. It offers no genuine insight into anything and is as pointless an observation as I can think of. As an alternative, I prefer, and am more comfortable with, silence. He doesn't. He thinks the best way to placate me, or soft soak me, is with inane chit chat. It just angers me more.

This sort of chat was rife at the moment. Both when I ventured out, and at home. You forgive the kids – to be honest they are happy to not initiate conversation if there isn't one there to be had. The less talking done to them, the more free time it gives them to go on their iPad and play these pointless little repetitive games they play. Ones where there is often no goal, as such, or no outcome. Just a whole load of singular, unsatisfying gaming 'transactions' they make, before it's on to the next one.

No, I can take it from the kids, but not from another adult. But right now, cooped up together, this was a regular occurrence. Chit chat – nothing to report other than perhaps did you see that so and so did such and such on Facebook? But this was how most days looked in lockdown. Chit chat, making food, walking the dog. Thank God for work of course. Although the actual quantity of work for us was drying up, it was giving us a reason to at least sit in different rooms.

His work dried up faster than mine by nature of what he does, working in an accounts department for a washing line company. I was continuing to work at a greater rate when he was just hanging around getting in the way. We have a WhatsApp family group with our brothers, sisters, and parents in for sharing photos of the kids, etc. I posted one yesterday on there of him having fallen asleep on the decking with his polo shirt riding up over his beer belly with the comment, "I thought Bernard Manning was dead – lol". It made me laugh so much I posted it on Facebook too and tagged him in it. He hates that but it was too funny to resist – and I even added the comment below, "if he doesn't ease up on these lockdown BBQ's, he will be #cholesterol." I don't care if he sees the funny side, or even likes it. A load of his mates from the football club joined in with the banter, taking the piss. Ended up getting 80 odd likes for it, so it can't just be me!

So, whilst I worked, as well as the regular things, that was pretty much the sum total of his day. BBQ, kids' games, walk the dog, TV. He didn't even run the household finances anymore. I took that off him as he was totally inept at it. This was a couple of years back. I had asked a question about what type of deal we were on with our broadband. He had no idea! Didn't even know the price of it. When I looked at it, we were paying probably double what we should have been paying for the speed we were getting. From there I looked at our energy bills, and – the same. It hadn't been updated in years. We had been shunted on to some standard rate when the discounted 12 months offer rate we took up when we moved to this house five years ago had lapsed.

The final straw was when I looked at the mortgage deal. Again, our fixed rate had come to an end, and we were languishing on a standard rate, and paying about 25% too much on our monthly payments. I was incandescent with rage.

We had lived in our previous house for about eight years, when unfortunately, my Mother had died. After we sold her house, me and my three brothers split the proceeds equally and it enabled us to put it towards the bigger house we now lived in. I had left it to him to manage the household financials – it's what he does for a living after all – and I was amazed to find that it had been completed neglected, and had exposed us to over paying on almost all aspects of our utilities and mortgage. All that money wasted. It seemed like my portion of the money my Mother had accumulated in her lifetime had been dishonoured in some way. She had enabled this house upgrade to happen, and here he was, frittering away money on the household bills - presumably because the inheritance had given him something of a 'free pass' and taken away his drive to better our situation.

There is no doubt in my mind, that if it had continued being left in his hands, we would be at serious risk of facing financial ruin with this type of inattentive approach. I gave him a nickname – 'Martin Lewis – the money saving expert'. Whenever he would so much as dare to comment on the value or question the price of anything, I'd say, "come on then Martin Lewis – money saving expert, what do you think a good price would be". And if the kids weren't around, "Fuck off Martin Lewis – money saving expert. We all know how useless you are on getting the best deal."

To try and teach him a lesson, and to see whether his focus had improved following this, I cancelled his direct debit payment for his credit card bill to see if he would even notice. He used the joint account as his primary account, and his credit card bill came out as a direct debit on the first of the month after his wages went in. As I was normally home from work first, I hid any letters that came from his credit card company, because I wanted him to find out of his own accord. Through his own initiative. Anyone with a mature approach to managing their money – and whose affairs were in order – would surely notice. If he passed the test, I told myself, then perhaps he could be involved in the household finances again in the future.

I had managed to access his online account portal too – changing the mobile contact number to mine so I could control the text alerts as well. I ignored the alerts, and I didn't answer my mobile to any unusual numbers that I didn't recognise. Sure enough, it took about three months before he realised that he had not been making payments on his account. It only came to light as I failed to hide a letter that was addressed to him, but this time from a collections agency; a company that I hadn't recognised. He unravelled it from there. This next part was beautiful. I didn't tell him that I had cancelled his direct debit. Instead I was able to ridicule him further – convincing him that he had cancelled it himself through his own stupidity and carelessness. Double bubble! It gave me plenty more opportunities to rub his nose right in it.

It was not a massive amount of money on this card, so he immediately settled up, got three months of penalty charges on top and a 'default' against his credit record. I logged on and changed the mobile number back to a similar number to his but switched the last two digits around so when it came to light the error could be explained away fairly easily. Potentially, it would have provided me with another chance to deride him further, however, he must have amended this and not mentioned anything to me. Like I said, it was a lesson that I hope he would learn from. It was no less than what he deserved anyway. It was his own fault.

Half an hour after they had left, the door clicked open signalling their return after walking the dog. I had heard them approach up the drive laughing about the fact one of the kids had tripped over the dog and landed in a bush. As they approached the door, I had heard him imploring the kids to stop laughing and to "shush now, no more laughing. We are home". Without any further encouragement, they entered the hallway in silence. Wow. Some consideration for me for once. I had mentioned I had a headache and hadn't wanted to go for a walk. How nice that they were taking my needs into account for a change.

I went out into the hall to speak to them. He avoided eye contact with me and concentrated on unlacing his shoes, and then taking the dogs lead and harness off. I always sense guilt when he does that. Normally I would suspect that, in this situation, it meant that he had stopped in the pub on the way round and had a pint while the children sat waiting with the dog in the beer garden. But there was no possibility of that at the moment. All the pubs were closed during lockdown – and even though I knew he got on well with the landlord, it was far too risky to consider letting anyone in. The pumps would have been decommissioned whilst they were shut, anyway, so it couldn't be this. Hmmm.

"Enjoy your walk kids?"

"Yes Mum."

"Ok, take your shoes off and go and wash your hands ready for tea."

"I'll do it," he offered. But no, he wasn't trying to be helpful, this was just a ploy to put some distance between us for a while, under the guise of keeping busy. He wanted to avoid my inquisitive stare. What was he up to?

"Don't worry, I'm doing it," I snapped at him. Do you really think that I'm some kind of idiot?

I took the kids through to the kitchen to clean up and make a start on tea. Something with vegetables. Something healthy and good for them. God knew that if I didn't take the lead on this then all they would eat during this lockdown would either be burgers or tinned food. I got the potato peeler out of the drawer.

"So where did you go guys?"

We had several different routes we used, all varying in length depending on what else we had planned. I thought I knew which one judging by the time it had taken.

"We turned right up the hill, then through Pandy Close, through the lane, and back down and around," said Elena.

Hmm, an unusual route that neither offered a decent length of walk nor passed any shops.

"We don't normally go that way," I replied.

The kids just shrugged. "We went past Monique's house. She was in her front garden on her scooter. We said hi to each other."

Of course. I fucking knew something was up.

Monique was Elena's school friend from her class. They were good friends – as much as 7-year olds can consistently be, with the constant playground politics that were always raging on

But it wasn't saying 'hi' to Monique that had pricked up my interest.

"That's nice. Was she in the front garden all by herself?"

"No, she was with her Mummy."

So transparent.

"OK, go and play in your rooms for a bit kids until I call you down." The kids ran off upstairs.

That explains why they went that route. There is no other reason they would go via the lane off Pandy Close. If you carried on, the road loops back around towards our house; it would make no sense to go this way. Plus, this way would take an absolute maximum of twenty minutes – even if you walked at the speed of Captain Tom around his driveway.

But now it made sense. Alison – Monique's Mum – was conveniently positioned in the front garden at that precise moment they passed by. Alison – a single mother who lived off her ex-husband's money, and routinely blew as much of it as possible on false nails and tanning studios. Worked four hours a day as a secretary in a Solicitors office yet enjoyed a life full of five-star foreign holidays and brand-new convertible Audi's. She just had her tits done last year too. Got to be at least a double E. I had looked at it before, and there was no way I could have afforded that – it was about six grand. Then again, maybe if I had managed the incomings and outgoings of our household, then it may have covered it. Suddenly I felt a rage at this thought, and it became my predominant reservation about this situation.

I walked into the lounge where he was now sat on the armchair. He must have sensed that there was going to be an argument, as he had pretended, he wasn't aware of me entering the room, but I saw him swallow hard.

"So where did you go on your walk then?"

"Just around the block," he replied – not looking up. Trying to keep composed and not look alarmed.

"Around the block, ok….our regular route?"

"Um, yeah more or less," he said – his eyes locked on to the TV as he absent-mindedly navigated the programme menu.

I marched over to him and swiped the remote out of his hand and spat in his face. That got his attention. He sat up in the chair and looked up at me. I looked at his face, and speculated to myself, 'I wonder if that is what a cows face looks like, moments before they get a bolt through their brain.'

"You went round to fucking see Alison didn't you?"

He scrambled in his seat to sit upright, my glob of spit still handing from his hair and cheek.

"Wha…what..who?"

"Don't you fucking 'who' me you lying slag. You know exactly who I mean. That Kardashian wannabe you were talking to. GO ON – deny it."

"I don't know what you mean….calm down."

"You fucking lying prick, of course you know what I mean. You fucking fancy her, don't you?"

"Please – keep your voice down the kids will here you." I was being quite loud now, but the red mist had descended. I couldn't control it.

I did tone my voice down, but just for effect, to sneer at him instead. How dare he. In daylight, in full view of the neighbourhood – and our children – he goes round her house to flirt! With each syllable, my head moved closer to his face.

"Fu-cking-ad-mit-it-cunt."

He pushed his head away from me into the chair and wiped his face for the first time with the back of his hand.

"Please stop. Don't be stupid. Of course not. It was just a route we took…. a change of scenery…. Elena suggested it…"

"Don't fucking lie to me!" I screeched in his face with no regard to whom could hear. In fact, I became completely unaware of my surroundings at all. All I could see was his face – there was no background.

"It's the truth…I didn't know she lived there…. please I beg you, keep it down."

"So, you're going to deny it still are you? Are you?"

With each 'are you', I jabbed my finger into his chest. He remained seated, and I stood over him. Towered over him. Dominated him.

"Look...I didn't know...all I did was say hello...I don't know..."

"DON'T LIE TO ME!" I pulled back my right hand, which was still gripping the potato peeler, and drove it forward – ramming it into his stomach. Blood squirted out like a triggered water pistol.

He screamed - as much as in surprise as anything. I dropped the potato peeler, probably in surprise too, and went out the kitchen to grab a towel. I brought it back into the lounge, but not before I noticed two worried, upset little faces peeking down through the spindles at the top of the stairs. I tightly shut the door behind me and made my way over to him. I put the towel up against the wound and pressed down firmly.

He winced and groaned, rolling back and forth in the chair in pain. "What the fuck have you done?"

"I'm sorry, I'm sorry," I instinctively said, just to comfort him and control his hysteria. "Press down on this, you'll be fine, it's nothing."

His eyes squinted and his mouth opened to reveal a clench of his teeth as he controlled the pain.

"Shall I get you some Ibuprofen?" I offered.

"Fucking Ibuprofen! You've fucking stabbed me. You're mad. Get me another towel."

I looked down at the first towel – it wasn't saturated, but it could do with replacing. Maybe something more substantial, like a bath towel. I quickly went upstairs to get one from the airing cupboard. On the way I passed the children – hugging each other on the landing, with tears rolling down their cheeks.

"What's wrong with Daddy?" said Lola.

I brusquely passed by. "He's had a small accident, he'll be okay, Mummy is just going to clean it up. Stay up here a minute."

I got the towel and ran into our bedroom to pick up the first aid kit that we kept in the wardrobe and ran back downstairs; shutting the door behind me.

"Here you go," I passed him the towel and took the previous one off him.

"What the fuck are you trying to do?" he said. It was a mixture of pain and sobbing. Like the sob of a broken heart. For a moment, I felt a sense of shame, but it passed. He had brought it on himself.

"I..just…want things to be right between us again," half sobbing myself. I struggled to find the conviction to match what had just transpired in that moment. I may have intentionally flashed some puppy dog eyes too.

"Go and see to the girls," he said, pulling the towel away from his torso to check how much blood had been absorbed into this fresh one. It had subsided.

I slowly stood up, and backed away a few steps: "Are you ok to deal with this?" I **was** concerned. I had made my point, and I didn't want his suffering to continue in front of the kids.

"Just look after the girls, I'm fine," he panted

I kept my eyes on him as I backed out of the room and shut the door behind me.

So, we are a week on.

We are still in lockdown.

We are still together.

A and E didn't strike us as an appealing place to go at this time, so we decided that as it was just a flesh wound, we would treat it as best we could at home. Added to that, we didn't want to be burdening the NHS further with our silly squabble. There were some people out there who desperately needed their attention, and they were working hard to ration their resources as it was, without us taking up their valuable time.

We certainly didn't anticipate any complications from the wound, but we knew that if any did manifest themselves in the weeks that followed, we would be able to go and see a Doctor then. He had some 'wound closure strips' (aka 'butterfly stitches) in his football holdall in the garage, so we just used these. We then packed it out well and changed the dressing regularly. It was no major issue.

Now it's all calmed down, I think on some level, I knew exactly what I was doing. I wanted to make my point – I wanted to be heard. The potato peeler – I know, essentially a knife – was only inserted maybe an inch. It is just a flesh wound, at the end of the day, and life will go on. We've got friends who have had worse DIY accidents than this – including one particularly bad incident with a chainsaw.

For the sake of the kids, we said that Daddy had been making kebabs for our next barbeque and had accidentally walked into a long skewer lying flat on the kitchen counter with the top pressed against the wall. When you demonstrate this, it looks feasible, and to anyone that you cannot demonstrate it to, it sounds too bizarre to not be true.

No one has asked any questions when we've told them – partly because we haven't seen anyone. But no one has asked any questions before when things were 'normal'…….

I didn't share it on Facebook either. I thought about it to add to the sense of reality – and also because I thought more of his football mates would mock him for it on there – but there seemed no sense in flaunting it.

However, yesterday, he did get a new friend request on there. From Alison. He hasn't accepted it yet, but he doesn't go on Facebook day and night to be fair. My sense is that he will accept it though. And then it will be interesting to see where it goes from there. My gut feeling is that they will start giving each other a few likes here and there – maybe on kids related things, or even general motivational-type quotes – then that will turn into messaging each other back and forth.

I then predict that Alison will maybe start getting a bit flirty with him. Maybe ending messages in a kiss (x), or perhaps the emoji blowing a kiss. I think that she will eventually ask him if he is happy in his marriage if his wife treats him well. This could then lead on to her offering a shoulder to cry on 'if he ever needs to talk x'.

It will be interesting to see how he responds if they ever get into that situation. How he answers some of these probing questions.

Fortunately, I will be able to witness the whole conversation. You see, Alison doesn't have a Facebook account. At least not one I could find. However, she does have an Instagram account, which allowed me to borrow some photographs to set up a Facebook account. I set it up with a pseudonym – and have planned to say, when 'Alison' is asked – that because I work at a Solicitors firm this was the guidance provided by her employer.

So, let's see if he's telling the truth then.

Or will he just say he was 'being friendly' and there is still nothing in it. Or maybe he won't engage with the request at all – but that would probably only be because he suspected something.

But I can assure him, it won't be a potato peeler next time.

The Demise of Ballbag

I felt the pulse of my mobile phone in my pocket likely telling me that I had received a message. Probably a WhatsApp video from one of the lads. Probably filth. Something like a very hot bird stripping off her clothes, with the big surprise at the end being that 'she's' packing a ten-inch cock. It would have to wait.

I felt a couple of follow up pulses in my pocket. It was definitely a post in one of the groups I was in with the lads. The most active one had me, Fiddler, Ox, Sanjay, and Ballbag in it; probably that one. It was usually Ballbag – he had the most time on his hands. Not the only thing he had on his hands. He hadn't worked – unless you include growing a couple of plants in his Mother's attic – in years. He'd gone into some detail on a night out once how he would go through four multipacks of Wotsits a day in between wanks. And how by the time his Mam came home his cock was orange.

I decided I would quickly check it out so that I could mute the notifications. I couldn't have my phone convulsing in my pocket for the next hour or so. I needed to work in silence.

I took out my phone and I had been right. I got the suspect and the room, but not the weapon. It was not a video of a dancing ladyboy exposing themselves, this one was of a talking nutsack. The nutsack had two eyes drawn on with a Sharpie, and a small wispy beard. Apparently identifying as male, the nutsack spoke as though he was inebriated, talking in an aggressive manner, and blurting out uncomfortable truths about Gary Neville.

It went on for over a minute, I had a general rule whereby I would only watch the sub twenty second videos on the go throughout the day, and anything longer than this I would make an appointment in my diary for later on that evening, when I could catch up on such substantial content Id accrued during the day at leisure – and possibly enjoy with a can of Stella.

As my stop was a few minutes away, I broke my golden rule and continued to watch. The nutsack first appeared to belong to someone very fucking old, I had thought. But after giving it some serious consideration, it really was too hard to call it.

The nutsack was being manipulated by a human hand from underneath to give it character and better on-screen presence. Apparently, correctly framed, by effectively smashing your balls together over and over between thumb and forefingers, running parallel to a soundtrack of dialogue, you could give the appearance on film that your nutsack is speaking. Holding court even.

The nutsack was very opinionated about politics, and Boris Johnson in particular – having more than a few choice words for BJ. This was quite a laugh until, as aforementioned, he decided to bring Gary Neville into it, and then I knew I had heard enough. How much spitefulness was that man expected to take? I acknowledged the exchange with a couple of emojis, and then muted the group for a few hours.

The first emoji was your standard laughing face with tears flying out each side to tell the guys – Ballbag especially – that I had enjoyed his little nutsack video. The second emoji was a simple thumbs up. This was more in response to the title endowed upon the video: "Meet my Dad – Nutsack." It worked on a couple of levels. I felt that the thumbs up emoji would be a classic – yet wholeheartedly appropriate - social media response to the comment.

I slid my phone back into the pocket of my denim jeans and stood up, extending my gloved hands towards the painted yellow rail in front of my seat and purposefully pressed the little red button that alerted the driver of my desire to stop the bus at the next available opportunity.

As the bus lurched and juddered through the narrow residential street, I began walking forwards to get to the exit. I put my dark glasses on, which steamed up with every breath that I took from the sanctity of my surgical face mask as the air forced its way out through the gap on each side of my nose, bringing sharply to mind the time I had a game of paintball with the lads.

I stood alongside the drivers' booth as he began manoeuvring the bus to a halt. The next five hundred yards that the driver and I covered in this formation had an air of tension, as - from no more than three feet away - we silently ignored the presence of one another.

The bus driver was a very fat man, wearing a white shirt that had long since been turned grey. He had dark patches of sweat around his collar and armpits, and beaded horizontal lines told tales of further perspiration that was occurring underneath each of his tits. I observed him breathing heavily through his mouth which hung open beneath a scruffy dark moustache. His bottle top glasses made his eyes look disproportionately large, and though he was probably only in his forties, he looked nearer sixty. His hair had been styled into place using the sweat of his brow, and the screen partition that had recently been put into place was already coated with a grimy discolouration and greasy fingerprints.

The bus began emitting a noisy hissing noise as the air pressure was released as the driver applied the brakes. For a second it looked as though he was going to rotate his face to my side to perhaps mutter something to me, so I turn to look the opposite way to avoid his glance.

The bus sidled up to its post situated outside a run-down looking washing line factory where my Dad worked for 40 years before he retired. Built in the 1970's, its dour, grey, two-storey frontage – once applauded as a good example of late 20th century architecture – was now a scourge on the landscape; nothing more than an example of architectural obsolescence. A row of equidistant single pane windows ran across each storey, and although recently painted, many of the frames were clearly rotten. Surrounding the building at its base were clusters of weeds – some so thick they could be classed as bushes. Cigarette butts littered the area outside the front door, which had a note handwritten in marker pen sellotaped to it, simply stating, "CLOSED DUE TO VIRUS".

The company was still in operation, but outwardly the signs were not encouraging. They would not be immune from the pressures most businesses were experiencing, or were going to experience, and if they were to vacate this property it would take millions of pounds in refurbishment to make it attractive for another business to lease. Small to medium businesses vied for spaces in modern premises, with comfortable, softer furnishings and large corporations wanted to occupy glass towers. With the limited natural light allowed in and outdated technological infrastructure it reeked of working/middle class, corporate misery. I felt sure that it was doomed and was only a matter of time.

I mumbled something resembling 'thanks' and stepped off the bus. My back to the bus, I kneeled and pretended to tie my shoe until I could hear the bus pulling away behind me. I glanced to my right, and watched it disappear out of view around the corner. No one else had gotten off at this stop. In fact, there had only been another three people on the bus the whole time I was a passenger.

Across the road from the bus stop was a Harvester restaurant. Of course, it was closed and its large bright yellow swing gate that denied entry to their car park was in place. There was nobody there. There was a little row of terraced houses a couple of hundred metres along from the factory.

My phone pulsed again in my pocket. Maybe a breaking news update. I turned the vibrate function off and decided that anything could wait until later.

I knew I could take a short cut through the grounds of the factory – everybody in the town used it. For years there had been a chain link fence at the rear of the building that had been snipped in several places and allowed people to pass through without any drama. All I had to do was to simply stroll through the car park, around the back and pass through the gap. It led to a small council estate behind the factory. I think that a blind eye had been turned to this unofficial entrance since many of the employees lived on the estate and this was their primary route to work.

I walked through the almost abandoned car park. To the right of the building I could see a few vans had been parked up whilst not in use. Two of them were neatly reverse parked against the perimeter fence. With the remaining one parked the other way I could see the signwriting on the rear door that humorously advised would-be thieves, "NO WASHING LINES LEFT ON THIS VAN OVERNIGHT." I chuckled.

"BATEMAN!"

Jeeeesus – I fair jumped out of my parka jacket as I heard someone shouting my name at the top of their voice. Unnecessarily so as well. As I spun around, I saw that my yodelling nemesis was no more than ten feet away from where I had been standing whilst silently tittering to myself about the van.

It was my friend, Ballbag.

I'd known him for twenty years, since school, and he had always looked like a repulsive bastard. His dark hair was long overdue a cut – even in normal circumstances – but now it sat swept back, held in place by the thick grease in which it suffocated. His skin was grimy like always, but now it seemed as though the grime had become embedded in the wrinkles he had developed in his later years, which made his forehead look like a small lined notebook that had been dropped in a dirty brook, and put on the radiator to dry.

His wild, scraggly beard – all uneven lengths and wispy renegade hairs growing in different directions, didn't imply overtones of wisdom and academia as some mature beards might. Neither was it the hallmark of a wild spirit or

Bohemian artist. His jaw was jutting out, and there was a self-satisfied sneer etched on his face. As I approached him, I even caught the scent of this hairy facial chin curtain. It was a strange combination of cigarettes, dead fish, and Vicks VapoRub.

He was coming from the direction of the 'goods in' shutters at the rear of the building. He walked with a slight limp, which made him do a funny little skip every other step. He was wearing a very worn Umbro football coat from the early 1990's. Very popular in their day, the coat had a base colour – say navy blue – and then a few layers of block V shapes in another colour – say red – from the collar to the bottom of the coat. The back of the coat had the same design, meaning that if the V's on the front and the back were lined up, it would form the diamond logo synonymous with the company. Although quite well looked after, considering, it was nonetheless very weathered, grubby, and some of the white padding stuff inside was hanging out courtesy of almost a foot-long tear in the seams.

"You twat!"

Ballbag gruffly laughed out loud. Considering his lack of concern about appearances, I was always amazed by his impeccable dentistry. Perfectly straight and in proportion, he had the best teeth of all my mates, even better than Fiddler – and he regularly visited a hygienist and flossed.

"Sorry Bateman lad. Didn't mean to scare you."

"The fuck you didn't."

"Haha – yeah s'pose I did."

"I was just on my way to yours. What you doing here?"

"Nothing much Bates. See that video of the nutsack I sent?"

"Yeah, yeah I saw it. Thought it was brutal about Gary Neville though." I paused, as his smell became quite overwhelming. "Christ Ballbag lad, when did you last have a wash?"

He did his short, staccato laugh that sounded like Woody Woodpecker.

"Dunno what you mean. I'm cleaner than a showering monk."

"A what?"

"Showering Monk."

"What the fuck is that?"

"You know – they do like karate and that."

"Showering Monk………OH!" – the penny dropped, "a Shaolin Monk you fuckwit."

"That's what I said. Anyway, come here." He beckoned me closer to listen more intently. He glanced from side to side and lowered his voice.

"I've got a bit of business going on in the washing line factory." A triumphant looking sneer unravelled across his face once again.

I coughed. "Spit it out mate, I can't be standing this close to you for long."

"My next-door neighbours boyfriend works in the warehouse in packing. Nice lad. Early twenties – fit as a fiddle, always down the gym, good looking bo-"

"I don't give a fuck about him Ballbag, get on with it!"

"Anyway, I sell him a bit of weed now and again and I was telling him a few months ago I could do with somewhere bigger to get more plants on the go."

I watched him lick his lips with excitement as he evidently seemed to be arriving at the point of this story.

"So," he continued, "when all this happened and the factory shut for a bit, he wanted to make up his money. He's got a set of keys to this place."

The smile across his face was as broad as can be now – like a predatory wolf who knew he had a small elk cornered. He emitted a short girlish giggle before continuing.

"I've got fifty plants up there! We're going to go halves!"

I leaned back out to take in some fresher air and chuckled, whilst slowly shaking my head.

"No leccy to pay for, and it's in a back room by the furnace. No one will be going in there until they open back up, and then we'll just get everything out overnight, nip it through the broken fence, and to my house. Come on – come and have a look."

He turned around and led the way to the rear of the building and the goods in doors.

"Shit, what's that?"

I stepped back sharply as I motioned up to what appeared to be a CCTV camera trained upon the shutter doors.

Without looking back, he began rummaging through his pockets and dismissively said to me, "Don't worry about that. It's a dud. The only real ones are a few on the factory floor, the front entrance and a couple of the offices on the second floor have them."

He paused, then turned around, and again with that broad grin, said, "and the way we go up and down this back stairwell, no-one will see us or know we are here."

He spun back around to the locked entrance door next to the larger shutters that would have been used for goods in deliveries. As he produced a keychain with several keys on from his pocket, a variety of stained, used tissues and sweet wrappers came out and fell to the ground as well. Ballbag stopped to pick up the tissues and coughed into one before stuffing them back into his pocket. I suggested to him he was a dirty bastard and that I hoped they weren't the same tissues he used for other activities when his Mam was at work. He laughed raucously just as he found the right key, and he turned it in the lock to open the door.

I followed him inside, and he locked the door behind me. We were stood in an unlit loading area. There was a service elevator behind us that was no doubt wide enough to accommodate a couple of pallets of goods alongside one another. The ground had an area of maybe 10 x 15 feet that had yellow lines painted in a criss-cross on the floor. To my right was a set of stone stairs that appeared to go up perhaps three or even four flights before expiring.

Ballbag had a sudden spring in his step as he skipped off up the steps and called behind him for me to follow him. With each passing step, he became more and more wired with the excitement of what he was about to show me - like someone had plugged him into the mains. I hadn't seen him this excited since Jane Porter (God rest her soul) had blown him off when we were pissed at the age of 17 years old at the back of the golf course. It couldn't have amounted to much the state he was in – and anyway she'd only offered to do it for a few swigs of his White Lightning and because she had heard his dog had died the week before and felt bad for him. We made that bit up to help him out, but she did get to down some of his tramp juice.

At the top landing, Ballbag froze, turned around slowly and in some kind of weird rhythm that resembled an expressive dance routine began rotating his hands around in small circles.

"Behold!"

He threw the door open and revealed a dis-used storeroom. In the corners of the room stood old rusted metal frames, benches and factory line tooling that had been stored here for years. In the middle of the room was a series of tents inside which sat his plants, underneath countless grow lamps which hung from above. Since it was all hooked up to the electricity supply from the factory, the endless tangle of extension leads and mains wires looked like the unravelled large intestine of ED209. They had not concerned themselves with using energy efficient LED lighting either. Large, high intensity bulbs doled out a blinding light that left a burning impression on your retina that took a while to dissipate completely.

At the back of the room were three small ventilation windows, no more than a foot in length. They were all propped open to provide some ventilation for this bumper crop. This, combined with one fan per tent, attempted to help remove the scent of the cannabis from the old used air in the room. I could see some carbon filters in front of the fans, but they must have since expired, as the room was pungent. There was almost a dozen - clearly complicit - two-feet high, white halogen heaters that were currently not in use, and which had all been herded into one corner of the room like a pack of confused, robot sheep.

After surveying the frankly modest grow, I looked back toward Ballbag. He was positively vibrating on the spot with excitement – periodically jerking forwards, seemingly involuntarily, as small spasms of excitement erupted in different parts of his body. Like the aftershocks of a seriously intense climax. When he saw I was watching him, he raised and lowered his eyebrows swiftly, three times.

"What you think?"

"I've seen bigger grows, but its ok. Nice little set up if I'm honest. Earn you a bit of pocket money lad as long as you don't get carried away and smoke it all yourself."

He told me – in an over-excited mumble that there was no danger of that, and that he would earn at least three grand from this once he split the profits with his business partner and paid back the people who had provided the equipment. It was difficult to follow, for as well as mumbling, his pitch and tone were inconsistent with the message he was conveying. Over emphasis on the wrong words, and unnecessary inflections drawing undue attention to forgettable parts of his monologue.

Most of the unintelligible words he uttered didn't even make it out into the open where they could be interpreted by a fellow human's brain who was receiving the data. It seemed like the words in his sentences clumsily jostled for position and came out of his mouth in the wrong order - and in all different directions. It reminded me of the Tommy Cooper piano player sketch. When he was challenged about the din he was playing on the piano, he insisted that he was playing the right keys - just in the wrong order. I visualised the words getting snared and hanging in the tips of the strands of his beard hairs - like cars I'd seen in pictures that were left hanging in trees following violent hurricanes.

I let him ramble on for a few minutes.

As I stared – periodically nodding as though I was listening – it struck me just how worthless this mans life was. He looked a mess. He drank too much. Smoked too much dope and had achieved nothing with his life. Just a piece of meat.

Still living in the bedroom he had grown up in and had never held down a proper job (just various irregular hustles for some cash to supplement his job seekers allowance). He had never helped anyone. Never done any charitable work. I had suspected that being with him and talking to him in person would soften me. Maybe change my mind. But no, it hadn't.

I would kill him as planned.

By now I had completely zoned out, nodding, open-mouthed, lost in my own thoughts. Even he could tell.

"Bates, you get me?"

I returned to my body and re-focussed on my prey.

"Yes Ballbag. I get you."

I began to slowly walk around him in a circle.

"I get that you are a scourge on society. I get that you survive on the basest, and most selfish of instincts. I get that you have no interest in improving yourself, or the lives of those around you."

I could sense the tension he was feeling as he completely froze for the first time, just his eyeballs moving. Transfixed to mine as I continuously paced. When they couldn't strain to the side anymore, his body would sharply turn by a quarter rotation to hold my stare and repeat the dance.

"I get that a successful day for you is shoplifting tampons from Asda and selling them to your neighbour. I get that you still steal from your Mother's purse to buy weed. I get that you think we call you Ballbag as a term of endearment."

I stopped right in front of him.

"I totally get it. And that's why I've come to kill you."

Ballbag paused and laughed out loud. I laughed out loud with him. We both laughed together. We pointed at each other, and heartily slapped each other on the upper arm in turns. The harder and longer I laughed, the more Ballbag continued to laugh. The laughing became hysterical in nature. The laughing became uncomfortable, and Ballbag was making the noise of laughter, but his eyes were not laughing anymore. His eyes grew wide and he looked panicked. I continued to laugh out loud, as Ballbag's laughter now began to wane. His trousers darkened as a stream of piss began to flow down his leg. I laughed harder, and harder, and harder as I drew out my chrome-headed hand axe.

I brought the sharp side down upon his head in a swift chopping action driven from the wrist multiple times. Maybe six, seven, eight or nine times. Chop, chop, chop. With each blow the axe went further through his cranium into the gooey soft substance underneath. It felt like cracking open a watermelon.

There were splatters of blood that became less and less as the blows progressed. It flew up on to my face, into my eyes, my hair. I didn't even pause to wipe it away. I just kept swinging the axe. It was a beautiful thing. It wouldn't take much to clean it up later. Some Dettol and an old tea towel first, then I would rub some chrome trim polish on to it to bring the shine up. The type that car detailers would use that I had picked up online. I would polish every inch of my beautiful axe so it looked as good as new – ready for the next time. I felt that it somehow meant I was honouring my victims: being bludgeoned by a newly shined, chrome handled axe. It would only take me ten minutes, anyway; it was well worth it.

Or was it something else?

I had started thinking that I was looking for something else. A long since departed emotion. Maybe I was trying to recreate that very first time I killed by returning my weapon of choice to its original state. When it was new and hadn't yet drawn any human blood. I laughed at the irony of the taking of my latest piece of meat. The first time I had used it had been on Jane Porter. Poor Jane. That was almost three years ago now. I had been lucky that first time. Learnt a lot too.

I paused and began breathing heavily. My heart used to beat right through my ribcage at this moment. Not anymore. I trembled a little but did not have to work too hard to maintain a composure. My brain was ravaged - like that a committed coke head. It had been exposed to so much dopamine, it could simply not return to its original state. The floodgates had been opened.

Ballbags lifeless torso had slumped to the knees and rested against my thighs and legs – head hanging down – the angle of his neck defying physics. I lifted my boot, and gently shoved it over to the ground. The soft, unremarkable bump it landed with was the pitiful exclamation mark that his life was deserving of.

Perhaps I needed to rethink this. Some higher calibre targets. People whose contribution would be missed. Even as a close friend of the victim, I probably wouldn't even get questioned about this other than in my capacity as a friend. Being surrounded by cannabis plants would probably lead them to the conclusion that he had upset the wrong people.

It wouldn't get much attention from the police.

Our gang would no doubt enjoy a good piss-up at some stage to 'mark' the untimely passing. And life would go on.

I was one step ahead. And my self-confession would have meant nothing.

I sat on a nearby pile of wooden pallets to catch my breath for a moment before leaving. I removed my phone from my pocket to turn it back on. As expected, I had a few notifications.

The boys in the WhatsApp group had found a video of some travellers' engaging in bare-knuckle boxing in the street, that they wanted to share. Sky News had shared a 'breaking news' update about a company making 2000 workers redundant. AOL mail let me know about several incoming pieces of correspondence. And I had a text message. Sent five minutes ago.

Don't really know anyone who sends me text messages anymore?

The first thing I noticed was the sender. NHStracing.

"You have been in contact with a person who has coronavirus (COVID-19). Log in to the NHS Test and Trace......"

I froze and looked up as realisation washed over me. How long ago did I get off the bus? Oh Christ. It was easily 30 minutes ago.

After realisation came the release, the rush that I had been craving. My hair stood on end, and I experienced a sudden explosion of visual disturbances and flashes of light in front of my eyes. I shook my head from side to side, but it did nothing to move the growing density of eye floaters teeming in my field of vision. These spots filled my eyes burying my retinas alive.

I became dizzy, and tried to get to my feet, but I slipped and crashed into the tower of pallets I had been sitting on – failing to recover my footing, and tumbling on to the soft, sticky corpse of Ballbag. I scrambled to get to my feet, but I only succeeded in slipping and sliding in his blood achieving no more than running uncontrollably on the spot with my hands on the ground either side of his head.

I flung myself backwards and began crawling across the floor instead. My right hand was stretched out in front of me as I felt my way forwards, using my other three limbs to walk like a disabled spider through the storage room floor – bumping into the occasional plant.

Still battling with my vision being encumbered alternately with shadows and bright lights, the sudden darkness as I scuttled around the floor terrified me. I had to get to a more well-lit area where I could assess my situation and ascertain a way out.

Through my screwed-up eyes, I could see cracks of light ten feet or so away. I gingerly kept moving forward, knocking over everything in my path in my panic to find a door to the outside world.

It was a door, but through the cracks of an intense, migraine-like temporary blindness I could still see the large chain that had kept it firmly closed for probably years. And I could see the sign.

This is not an exit.

The Postman

Everyone was allowed one form of exercise per day. That pretty much gave people a choice of walking, running, or cycling.

All the golf courses and tennis courts were closed as far as I was aware. No dry ski slopes open. Gyms and recreation centres - all closed. Shame, I did frequent such facilities often.

There was no guidance on the length of time this exercise should, or could, take. If you were to apply a bit common sense then it would be reasonable to suggest that – health permitting – perhaps a walk, run, or cycle for around 30 minutes to an hour represented a decent level of exercise.

I would probably have a requirement to go out up to several times a day, but I guess if I did three shorter bursts of exercise, say 20 minutes each, then it could be argued that I was only doing the minimum amount of exercise that we were entitled to in a 24 hour period? That sounded fair didn't it?

It was also unlikely - with the policing in the country already stretched to breaking point before the pandemic - that in the balance of probabilities I would run into the same police officer, in the same or alternative locations, more than once per day.

And then they would have to remember me.

And that would only matter if they had even recognised me in the first place amongst the endless procession of other lycra'd up individuals – many of them wearing some kind of guards around the lower half of their heads; often snoods, banishing about 60% of their facial surface area into complete obscurity.

I had ordered a couple of different pairs of three-quarter length, lycra, cycling shorts that were delivered to my home address. I had given this some thought. It was still March and bloody cold, so I wasn't about to wear shorts. Not like those mad blokes you see wearing shorts no matter what time of year it was. I always think of that as an open invitation to a pissing contest. Although Spring was supposed to be beckoning, it was only a couple of years ago that it was heavy snow in March so I wasn't being caught out – I didn't know when I could get more if I needed to. I had chosen cycling over walking or running for speed.

There were some other rules about our exercise entitlement too.

Go alone – or only with members from your household. No problem sticking to this. This was fine. As were gatherings of more than two being subject to police enforced dispersals, and even perhaps being fined. If anything, this helped normalise potentially otherwise suspicious looking situations.

Keep two metres apart from anyone outside of your household. Not sweating it on this. Requires a bit of effort to remember and employ, and far from ideal, but it's not too far away so that it causes a 'communication' problem. And anyway, the chances of someone with the infection being out and about 'exercising' was low I thought. None of this is ever risk free.

Stay local. There were to be no unnecessary journeys in your car, period, so all exercise was encouraged to be carried out locally and using open spaces. This could've been slightly tricky, however, in more general terms, the first new rule of this lockdown was that you should 'only travel if you absolutely cannot work from home'. Loophole? Didn't want to be working from home really.

In fact, apart from the encouragement to use your garden for fresh air and exercise (even though I lived in a 4th floor apartment and had no garden - this would never have worked), all those guidelines were highly adaptable for me.

Then of course there was my nan. A vulnerable, single, elderly person.

My nan was all I really had. Raised me since I turned 9. Proper tough. Lived through it all, still had all her faculties about her – and her acerbic wit hadn't aged. She wasn't buying into all this. "I've survived Hitler, Hippies and Miners Strikes." The government warnings were not sinking in. Luckily, all her friends were in their 80's too and they had all decided to pay more attention to the guidance on self-isolating, so she was left alone largely by virtue of that. I was the only family who kept in touch, so I stayed away too, for her safety. I told her I had some symptoms because she wasn't having any of it at first.

That was of course, apart from the essential shopping trips I had to make on her behalf so I could look after her. That gave me further opportunities to get outdoors – even if it meant walking was the best means of achieving this.

I could visit the Tesco Metro nearby (about a two mile walk) fill up a bag with some essentials, and fresh produce, then take it over to my nans (about another mile in a different direction) who lived on a nearby council run estate, mainly comprising of high rises. I'd leave it under a single white plastic garden chair on the landing of her floor and give her a ring when to open her door and pull it inside.

The first time I did this I walked off before she had come out to claim it, and before she had chance, some little bastards who lived in the same block had grabbed it and run off with it. I beat myself up badly about that one. How could I have been mugged off like that? By some little kids? Of anyone, I should have known better.

Now, she opens the door, gives me a wink, tells me what a "good boy" I am, and hurries off inside again. She can't manage WhatsApp, but she can just about send an often-nonsensical text listing a few bits she needs every few days. She has said to let the list build up and just to do a drop off once a week for her would be fine, but to be honest, it suits me to pop round to her estate as many times as I can.

My social media is going mad at the moment. Everyone is bored, I think. What do they say? The devil makes work for idle hands. Whoever came up with that phrase definitely had social media whilst self-isolating in mind.

God knows how many countless collective hours – billions, it has to be – people have spent endlessly scrolling through social media, instead of being productive. The level of activity in group chats is through the roof. If I've received one meme, or funny short video, I've received hundreds. And, if I'm honest, send back almost as many too.

I'm still working – as best as I can anyway. Loads of my friends literally cannot work at all. The minute their business closes, there is nothing they can do from home. How can an industrial welder do anything from their front room?

So, most people I know are kicking their heels. Watching Netflix and looking for things to mend around the house. And drinking too much. Quite a few people seem to have increased their drinking. If only to distinguish between day and night! There's a new app doing the rounds where people can remotely drink and party in a virtual space, whilst in the safety of their own homes.

I think I actually have got some symptoms now. Been feeling a bit hot. Feels like my glands are up.

But I've got to keep going. I've got too many people requiring my assistance.

And I can't afford to stop and let my customers down. Or my suppliers. People are fickle. They'll just go somewhere else.

No – got to power through and keep going. Perhaps I'll take my bike over to my nans estate for the drop off instead. Get back home as soon as I can. Get myself into bed.

I could do without being laid up for a fortnight.

These bags of coke aren't going to distribute themselves after all.

The Yield

The huge barn door was in no fit state for 'slamming' as such – it was way too large, too heavy and in too poor shape to withstand the tremors. Instead it was dragged to a close with the top section of wood flapping away behind it. Once in the locked position, I could hear the wooden barricade being drawn across, followed by the sound of the heavy-duty chain being interwoven through the handles. The lock was clamped together, and I heard the key turning in the barrel. A quick tug to check the integrity of the blockade was followed by the vague smell of smoke from a freshly lit cigarette, then the sound of footsteps on a dusty, gravel surface trudging off into the distance.

Then, apart from the vague sound of a nearby rat scurrying around, all fell silent.

From memory, the barn was about ten acres away from the nearest road – just under half a mile. From here, all you could hear was the feint rush of the occasional large truck passing by, or maybe the angry wasp-like sound of a sports motorbike now and again. There was dense woodland in the other direction.

In the morning you could hear the cockerel crowing right across all four corners of the farm. It was not too pronounced from this distance – as the cockerel resided near the pigs' enclosure. I figured that the clocks must have gone forward a couple of weeks ago to herald the start of British

Summer Time. I had noticed that he would start crowing even earlier – usually around 4am.

It didn't bother me. In fact, it gave me some comfort in a weird way. It was one of just a few constants in my life that was helping me establish some kind of routine. But on the other hand, it also made my mood black as I awoke to the realisation of my situation. I would swallow hard in trepidation of the day ahead, and about how this would end.

Today was what I considered to be a 'good' day. I know Seth is not comfortable with any of this. He tries to avoid looking me in the eye and we don't talk anymore. We are both in our early twenties and used to share lots of conversations – mainly about our love of metal music – and sometimes boxing or MMA, but lately I just seem to get one-word answers from him.

Sometimes, we would share a joint at the end of the day around the back of the barn, hiding from his dad, but there was no chance of that now. I even gave him some cool ideas for his sleeve tattoo I'd been saving for myself – going so far as to sketch out this gnarly bio-mechanical skull with pistons protruding from its eyes, which he had gone and gotten done. I would go so far as to say we were pretty good friends, although I had only known him for just over a year. We had even talked about going to a music festival this year in Belgium together........I guess it will end up getting cancelled anyway.

With the coast being clear, I took off the sack that gets placed on my head every night at 'lock up' time. It's for my own good, I am informed, and I am permitted to remove it as soon as I can hear that the barn is locked. The smell of damp hangs around, as I swot at my face to remove all the tiny loose filaments of rope that is its legacy, and pinch at the pieces off the end of my tongue that I had inhaled.

I looked down at my right leg. For a fleeting moment I feel a mild wave of optimism – the kind that you experience when you briefly entertain winning the lottery. But this is followed by the exact same kind of reality check seconds later. The makeshift shackle is still there, attached to the few metres of chain. I give the chain a tug – just in case – but I am met with the same disappointment as when I tried this yesterday. The steel post it was attached to still had a shine to it, and where it had been recently concreted into the ground there was not the accumulation of many years of built up grime and mud across it. Unlike everywhere else in this dilapidated barn.

I had returned to work at Cane Hill Farm in February, and I had been holed up here for around four weeks now. I had left the farm last Winter to return home for a few months, to see my family and friends. By comparison to home, the money doesn't really go that far anymore, and things are far more complicated now following their Brexit situation. But I had enjoyed my time there. Made some new friends (or so I thought), and we had made plans for 2020 that sounded fun and that I wanted to honour. And I was only 22. Another year of this, and then maybe I would go home with a little bit of saved cash and try and start my graphic design career. I didn't intend to be a farm hand cum fruit picker all my life.

There was one other reason of course – Mya. She lived in the next town – just a ten-minute bus ride. The bus stopped right outside the farm – near the guest annex, where I used to live. Five or six miles down a winding, hedgerow lined single lane carriageway – fields all around – and it would pull up outside a little post office, and I would walk from there. I used to love cycling there and had borrowed Seth's bike sometimes to make the journey. But the days on the farm were long, and in the last few months before I went home, I just wanted to get to her as quickly as possible.

The best way to describe how she looked is to say she looked like a Disney Princess. She was beautiful with long black hair, and big expressive brown eyes. And smart. She was doing her final year in Law School in the London School of Economics! Our meetings were largely clandestine – and it wasn't hard to see why. Her Dad was not keen on the situation. And if I'm honest, I don't blame him. She had everything going for her. Looks, personality, a potentially fantastic career. Their home was modest, so I felt certain that her family must have made many personal sacrifices to support this ambition. So why would he welcome the news that she was in a relationship with a Romanian fruit picker from the farm up the road?

I didn't take it personally. I also didn't really believe it would last. But while it did, I was going to hang on to it for dear life for as long as I could. If she hadn't had gone back to University, then I may even have stayed through the Winter somehow. But I had been looking forward to when she returned in April, and spending time together through the Summer. When I had last spoken to her, sometime in the middle of March, it had been indicated to the students that they should return to their family home as a lockdown seemed imminent. Other countries had already done so.

When the reality of a lockdown hit home to me, it felt like an approaching tsunami. I imagined looking out over a calm sea, when on the horizon, I became aware of something. The movements were more aggressive, and the sea level looked higher. As it got ever closer, all the birds in the sky begin squawking and hooting – beating a hasty retreat towards land. When you realise the size and scale of what you are facing, it is too close, and coming at you too fast to get out of the way. And it was too fast for me to get out of the way.

I had booked a one-way flight home. The only one I could get had a connecting flight at the Schiphol in the Netherlands. It was scheduled for the following day in late March, although I was still anxious about whether it would go ahead. As a result of the limited passenger clarity, I had no option but to travel down to London by train and hope for the best when I got to the Airport, although I expected further complications. And I did get complications, though not the ones I was expecting to get.

I would never claim that I was treated like 'one of the family', but I would occasionally be invited into the main farmhouse to eat – usually on a Sunday. Agnes would cook a huge roast dinner, and there were always leftovers that the pigs polished off afterwards. The four of us, me, Seth, Agnes and her husband Elmer would eat in the stone floored kitchen on a huge wooden table about ten inches thick that looked like it was once used in the banquet hall of a castle, five hundred years ago. It looked like it would take at least eight men to lift it. The only source of heat would be the fireplace, and Elmer liberally tossed logs on it throughout the meal – the blackened chimney stack testament to the height the flames sometimes reached.

Elmer was a fearsome man. He stood at least six feet five tall and had the frame – and stance - of a silverback gorilla. His hands were ridiculously enormous, which I felt could have easily snapped my wrist if one of his albeit seldom handshakes became too enthusiastic. They were calloused and shiny from the years of farm work. He had a bald head, and a long, thick beard – the grey hairs having taken over the black. I put him at about sixty years old. Highly economical with his words, he would simply prefer to train his intense gaze on you to communicate.

It was during these moments that I first became aware that the farm could be under some financial pressure. The farm had a shop, run by Agnes, that sold organic meat from the animals on the farm, but the main part of their business came from their crops. I had been taken on at the start of the lambing season as a labourer, and then as the months moved on, I would move on to picking soft fruits, then salads and other vegetables. I would pick, pack and grade them, and move them into the storage area ready for collection.

It was a given that margins were slender, but any interruption could prove devastating. And this was realised around late October. Most of Cane Hill's one hundred acres were left under flood water when it suffered six months of rainfall in just six weeks. The majority of the winter vegetables, such as potatoes, cauliflowers and cabbages were ruined. They were left to rot in the field, and it also meant Elmer had been unable to sow wheat.

Seth had told me that the farm had been in the family for generations, and when conversations had come up about selling the farm a few times over the years and cashing in, they had always been brief. He said his Father had always been very clear that he intended to die on this farm, and nothing was going to get in the way of that.

When I had been putting the produce into storage, I had heard the odd terse conversation about money taking place in the farm shop between Elmer and Agnes, although once they knew I was nearby they would cease the conversation. I would always make more noise than necessary to give them advance warning I was there to avoid any awkwardness.

Whilst I didn't have a warm relationship with either of them, I was treated fairly. They expected me to work long, hard hours, but this was all laid out at the start, and I had lodgings and was paid on time. That's what got me there, and what kept me coming back was Mya, and my friendship with Seth. I couldn't seem any huge resemblance to Elmer in him – neither physically, nor in his mannerisms. He had long, wavy dark hair, and a tall, skinny frame.

I think Seth was happy to have me around. Some of the previous people who had come and gone hadn't spoken English, or he just not made a connection with them. We were a similar age and liked doing the same things. His parents treated him like an employee rather than a son, so we naturally gravitated towards one another.

We would spend most of the day together, doing our jobs, then often head up to the barn in the evening with a Bluetooth speaker and – usually – a nice bag of green in the evening. On the weekend, we would head into town and check out the pubs - this is how I met Mya. Once I had begun spending more and more time going to see Mya, I had detected a slight resentment, maybe jealousy, from Seth. I was probably too caught up in my own pursuits to pay it much attention, but I could sense that our relationship had – not completely soured – but nonetheless changed.

When I first arrived back at the farm, Mya was still at university, so I enjoyed the opportunity to get reacquainted with Seth. We had resumed our evenings at the barn talking, smoking, listening to music. He was still a little bit frosty toward me at first, but I figured he would loosen up the more time we spent together. It was a slower process than I anticipated, however, and I was still sensing some distance between us.

It was when Mya had messaged me about the likelihood of returning home to stay for the duration of lockdown, that I first had mentioned that I had better start thinking about returning home to Romania. I made this statement freely and openly, without any real thought. As far as I could tell, this was the obvious and necessary thing to do, and would not come as a surprise to anyone. However, Seth did express some shock and disappointment at this. I put it down to the fact that he had been enjoying my company and took it as a compliment.

That night, I didn't smoke too much and walked back down to the guest annex after about an hour to start Googling flights home and put some kind of plan together. I was lying on my bed with the TV playing, looking at my phone, when I heard the lock in my door gently click; the familiar sound of it being unlocked with a key from the outside. I sat up in the bed, muted the TV and stared at the door. There were a few moments of complete silence, then an almighty crash, as the door was smashed open against the wall.

My heart raced and I instinctively scrabbled up the bed to be furthest from the door. The room just contained a bed, a chest of drawers on which the TV rested, and a small sink area. It simply took three large strides to get through the door and to the bed. And that is exactly what Elmer did when he burst in, shotgun in hand, face contorted with rage. I had never seen so much expression etched on to his face than I did now with this display of frenzied fury.

I had words I wanted to say, questions I wanted to ask, but my mouth simply hung open, gasping in the face of this overwhelming hostility. Adding to the sense of horror, was the fact that he was wearing a blood splattered apron from working in his slaughterhouse. His face was clammy, he was breathing heavily through his wide-open mouth. He looked like he was having a rush of some kind.

Pointing the shotgun at me, he panted, "Get up."

"E..Elmer..." was all I could manage

He rocked from side to side on his feet, nervously glancing around the room and back from where he came.

"On your fucking toes now!" he roared back at me.

All I can remember next, before I fell unconscious, is that I tried again to speak, before the force of the butt of the shotgun, hitting me square in the side of my temple put me to sleep. I still don't know how long for.

When I awoke, I was hog tied and recognised my surroundings as the top barn. It was dark outside. I tried to stay calm and assess what was going on. I could feel dry blood cracking on my face when I moved my facial muscles, and when I raised my head, I could see a small pool of it had dried on the floor beneath me. There was some light coming from the other side of the barn from some kind of lantern.

I squinted my eyes to try and see more clearly, in the way that I would after waking up in the morning following a heavy night. From the light of the lamp, I could see the frantic figure of Elmer appearing to be digging, or something, perhaps fifteen metres away. For somebody who seldom spoke much at all, I could hear him constantly mumbling away to himself. His work rate was fearsome, at first a pick, and then a shovel hammering down on the ground. In the shadows I noticed that that Seth stood there, holding the lantern allowing his Father to work. He remained completely still, and silent.

I tried to wriggle around, but there was no way I was going to get out of this knot to allow any kind of grand escape. What was he digging? Was it my grave? I always thought he looked unhinged. Was Seth in on this? My mind raced, and panic overcame me. I yelled out, "Let me go."

With his back still to me, Elmer stood up and straightened up, dropping the shovel to the ground. His frenzy replaced with an eerie calm that was in some ways more chilling. He remained this way for what was probably seconds but felt like minutes. Eventually, only visible by the light of the lamp, I saw him outstretch his arm and beckon Seth to follow him. He turned around, slowly peeled off his leather rigger gardening gloves and threw them do the ground.

As he slowly approached, with Seth keeping pace behind him, I could see the determined look on his face. I knew that he was committed to whatever course of action he had decided upon. As with selling the farm, his mind was un-changeable, and he would go through with whatever he intended no matter what.

He got to within touching distance of me and, with his boot almost touching my chin, I craned my neck back as far as it would go to look at him.

"Elmer, please, let me go. I will disappear back to Romania; you will never hear from me again."

Elmer sighed, then as quick as a cat – which was shocking for a man of his size – he shot down on one knee, grabbed my hair and pulled my neck back for me, holding it there.

"You listen to me, you dirty little fucking snollygoster. I gave your stinkin' immigrant arse a fucking job on my farm – somewhere to live – I had you in my home! And this is how you plan to repay me?"

He was hissing between gritted teeth; particles of spit and phlegm intermittently flying out over me.

"You think you can just walk away and leave me? You want to ruin my farm? You want to ruin me? You will not do that. You will not do that, you filthy fucking dog." He broke away only to hock up a sizable amount of phlegm and spit it in at my brow. The thick clump hung down across my left eye.

"Elmer," I gasped, now struggling to breath properly with my head being tightly yanked back. "I'm not trying to ruin you. I wanted to help you on your farm, but I must go home. This…. sickness is coming…"

He levelled up our eyeline and stared at me with his intense, dead gaze.

"You are not going anywhere you stinking cunt. You are staying here, and you are going to pick my fruit and veg. I own you now."

As a full stop, he slammed my face into the stone floor and let go of my hair. I was unconscious again.

When I next came around, dawn was breaking. My eyes scanned around, there didn't appear to be anyone else around. I was lying in a foetal position – this meant I was no longer tied up. I sat up and outstretched my arms. I shrieked out in pain as I realised how many deep and sore abrasions they were covered in from the rope. But at least I was untied. The sense of relief was short lived, and I tried to stand up. At first, I thought my right leg was snagged on something, or it had somehow been injured in the scuffle. But when I tended to it, my heart sank.

And this makeshift cell has been my home ever since. I get food and water brought to me first thing in the morning, and last thing at night (I think it's the leftovers that the pigs used to get), and I work on the farm in the day. With close supervision from either Elmer or Seth, of course. Either of whom are always armed with a shotgun around me.

On my first morning like this, Seth brought me a bucket of water and some rags for cleaning myself up with. I was in a hell of a mess – probably had a concussion too from the blows to the head. I begged him to help me. I pleaded with him and promised that I would quietly run away through the woods, hitch-hike into the city and they would never see or hear from me again. I would cause no trouble for them. I understood that they had problems and were stressed to the max when they had done this. That they were honourable people, and this was not them. It was not too late.

Elmer had clearly given him strict instructions to not speak to me at all. Seth abided by these rules – which was no surprise to me having personally seen his tyrannical side. It confirmed what I had believed all along that Seth had a deep fear of his Father.

Elmer only ever spoke to me to grunt his instructions. The first few times I was in his presence, I had tried to reason with him, but on each occasion, it was met with a stiff smash across the face with the butt of his shotgun. There was no argument, discussion or attempt at justification. And more interestingly, it was delivered with no anger, or emotion of any kind. Of course, I learned to stop and instead just followed orders, and that worked at maintaining the calm. Elmer never tormented me – physically or verbally. I just had to get the work done.

On the seventh day, Elmer paid me a rare visit in the barn. Expressionless, he walked over to me, and tossed an envelope down at my feet. I immediately recognised the envelope as the type he used to give me my wages in.

Muttering only, "I'm not a fucking thief," before he sauntered slowly out.

Physically, I'm ok. My bruises have healed, and I don't seem to have any lasting damage. They brought up my clothes in a suitcase. I have some blankets and pillows here, so I can keep warm in the night. I'm allowed to shower once a week in a shower block (which is what I used to use before). It has no windows and one of my captors sits outside with the shotgun while I'm inside. They keep me away from razor blades and scissors, so my hair and beard are getting long, but I suspect I will be sheared like a sheep if it takes their fancy.

But what keeps me up at night, is the fact that the longer this goes on, I think the outcome for me gets worse.

I feel sure they have reported me as a missing person. Lots of people in the town knew I was here. I saw some of my belongings in the dumpster when I was cleaning out the hen house. Nothing important, magazines, a bobble head Freddie Mercury, some other things. When I had last weeks shower, armed with bottles of bleach, Agnes was cleaning the guest annex with a degree of thoroughness I don't think it had experienced before.

I'm not sure if the pandemic is over? If lockdown is even still ongoing? I worry about my family in Romania. I only have my Mother and a Sister now. I had told them back in March that I would be coming home, and that was the last contact I made with them. Nothing made me so upset as thinking about what they were going through. They would be sick with worry. They had no idea where in the world I was, and if I was dead or alive. They knew where I worked, and they would have rung. What had they been told? Probably that I had left to return home.

Mya would think I had abandoned her and returned home without so much as a message saying goodbye.

How does this end? This question fills me with fear.

Maybe nobody noticed – the world was too preoccupied. I could be kept here for 10 years or more. That would make Elmer around 70 years old then. Would Seth develop his Fathers temperament, take the reins of the business, and keep me in enslavement for even longer?

Or do people start asking questions. Unwelcome visitors start coming around, and Elmer just finishes me off and feeds me to the pigs. He could brain me with a mallet and dice me up in his slaughterhouse quite easily.

I need to plan my escape. Perhaps I need to keep talking to Seth, perhaps he can be turned.

I need to shake them off and get into those woods. Once I'm in there, I will have a great chance of losing them between the trees and escaping.

I will run to Mya's house and she will help me.

Nuthin But A G'Thang

Ok, so my background is not in virology, physics or engineering. I am, however, a lecturer of Sociology. And my philosophy, is that after completing an education to a Doctorate level it does give one the type of credibility to comment on matters outside of your specialism. To study, and achieve to this level, for a significant period of time activates the kind of enquiring mind that gives you the right to ask questions. It gives you the right to stir up debate. And one should not be dismissed or excluded from the conversation, simply because it was not a specialist subject that I studied whilst in formal education.

As a true scholar, I am constantly studying and learning about all manners of different subjects. Technology, science, psychology – these are amongst the subjects that I am extremely well read on. I have not studied toward a formal qualification on each of these topics – it would simply not be possible - but in my opinion, that makes me no less a so-called expert that anyone else.

I appreciate that, for instance, I do not have a comprehensive understanding of the complex chemical processes involved in actually manufacturing medicines, so I would not presume to tell a pharmaceutical engineer his business when mixing drugs. This would require a very specific knowledge, and of course there must be a requirement to test this knowledge to some kind of universal standard. But I don't believe that I need this same level of knowledge, or formal background, to be able to comment – and have a totally valid opinion - on the debate of whether we, as a country, should significantly reduce our use of antibiotics, for example.

Not at all. What I would need to be able to do that, would be to become a scholar on the subject. Someone who absorbs every piece of information that they can about something, and assesses it analytically, in an unbiased fashion. And this is where my naturally inquisitive mind – bolstered by many years of study, and a respect for the fact that volumes of information should be harnessed – becomes completely immersed in finding out every fact and point of view on any given subject before I would comment.

I've read dozens of journals, detailing many different scientific studies and alternative opinions from medical experts that I believe I have collated enough expert opinion, and am able to combine it with some of my own analysis to assimilate my point of view. I don't come to conclusions lightly, and I vociferously believe in what I am saying.

So, let's make no mistake here: I'm not your average, random, Facebook friend who, seemingly overnight, becomes an expert on all things political, for example. Knowledge is my lifeblood.

Therefore, I am not joking when I say that, I fully believe installing 5G networks is accelerating the spread of the virus.

Some people have tried to portray me as some kind of a crazy person, and to classify me alongside Area 51-type promoters, whose ideas (which I'm not dismissing!) are all deep-rooted in 'conspiracy theory' territory. My words have been twisted in a direct attempt to discredit me and undermine my position, which I have arrived at after completing thorough research. As well as to create sensationalist news stories. I've also been told it is panicking the nation to say such things.

But I don't care about that. In fact, I take it as a compliment, and as testament to the fact that I must be on to something. A couple of months ago, nobody knew who I was. Now it seems as though I'm being quoted in newspapers or online journals on a daily basis. My Twitter feed, where I've shared lots of my research, has grown from 33 followers to over 5000 in a month. Celebrities, I've never met (or even enjoyed, in some cases) are quoting me. Not so keen on the latter to be honest – I feel as though by piggy backing me, it gives them a route to become an 'instant expert'.

The basis for these ideas that many people are so quick to dismiss is as follows. Many studies show that Electro-Magnetic Radiation (EMR) suppresses the immune system. A suppressed immune system helps viruses and bacteria thrive. So, if we are putting up lots of 5G masts around the country at the moment, then it follows that 5G by proxy – could act as an accelerator the for virus.

That's it. That's the premise of it. It is supported by over 200 scientists and doctors from over 40 nations.

Many of the detractors would point out this is not conclusively proven. There may be studies out there that suggest that this is not the case, too. But the point is that surely, we should be acting with far more precaution, and that there should even be a temporary prohibition on erecting these masts until such time we can prove beyond a doubt that they are safe? Surely the burden on proof is on the 5G operators to prove I am wrong?

Some quarters seem happy to accept that whilst they admit the 5G radio frequency is indisputably higher than the 4G, it is still a significantly lower level than the one which can be dangerous to humans. The telecoms companies apparently make use of a non-ionising spectrum which cannot penetrate cells to mutate DNA. How reassuring.

I would far prefer our UK government – who are determined to have a world leading 5G infrastructure (to go with their very fast train) and driving this initiative through forcefully – to categorically describe it as safe after a series of scientific consultations or though time-tested studies. Instead of doing that, Public Health England issued a quote containing the following line: "...the overall exposure is expected to remain low relative to guidelines and, as such, there should be no consequences for public health. "

'Should' be? Wow. And nobody is concerned about this lack of conviction? Nobody agrees with me – and of course many others – that this should perhaps be tested first so we can make a more definitive statement about it. In fact, those of us in agreement on this seems to get derided as tin-foil-hat wearing conspiracy theorists. I want to hear something like the statement we can confidently make about our fibre optic connections, which is simply this: "It is totally safe and poses zero threat to health." Now that's a statement you can take to the bank.

Until they can, I think we are within our rights to consider this as a clinical experiment. Informed consent is a medical term whereby a patient is made clear of the risks before any clinical trial, or medical procedure is carried out on them.

There is even a UN international covenant on this pertaining to civil rights that clearly prohibits anything less than full disclosure to test subjects. You can see where I am going with this.

The UK's Independent fact checking charity fell over themselves to quickly debunk this theory on their website, but in my opinion even they got side-tracked into the conspiracy theory element of it all and as a result, the conversation strays from the core theme and gets bundled in with another theory. The theory that viruses can communicate with each other when making decisions about infecting a host.

It started from a sensationalist headline in a rather low rent tabloid newspaper. They had picked up on my comments I had made about EMR suppressing the immune system and combined it with another theory they had found - from a 2011 research paper. This was written by several academics and hypothesises that bacteria may produce electromagnetic signals to communicate with other bacteria when making decisions about infecting a host. You can see how this could be manipulated by a crafty journalist to produce quite an eye-catching story. And also, how some of the words and phrases could be substituted for others to make it all sound quite ridiculous – and make me guilty by association having been spoken about within the same article.

So a considerable number of people now associated me with this headline 'spin' on what I said to make it sound like I was claiming that, "5G masts can spread viruses", projecting images in peoples' imaginations of these ugly masts blighting our streets and countryside, somehow 'beaming' diseases from post to post. The virus' reach growing each time it was relayed along.

What they are doing to me, and people who share my concerns, is quite clever really. The propaganda is spread by way of what is little more than a whisper campaign across social media platforms, radio phone ins – even editorials in trade magazines for the telecoms industry. They all 'educate' people to balk the minute they hear 'Virus' and '5G' within the same sentence. To instantly dismiss it without question; for the minute they do question it they fear being met with ridicule.

In an increasingly divided society, and in an era of the phenomenon of 'fake news', it is also difficult for a person to feel qualified to give an opinion. Sometimes it is better to just sit an argument out if you are not sure and leave to the 'people who know what they are doing.' That can surely be the only reason that people are not rioting in the streets about the UK governments decision to involve the Chinese telecoms giant, Huawei, in providing the technology to establish the 5G network? How can anyone deny that this is a high-risk vendor, and that forging a partnership in this way raises serious security issues for our country. That's before you begin talking about the human rights concerns they should legitimately assess.

So even if the science I back is not exactly right. Even if it is proven that the electromagnetic radiation given off by operating 5G networks is not harmful (I wish). And even if the chief inconvenience of 5G is the unsightly masts. I think that there is still something that they are not being straight with us about.

It could be about our civil liberties. It will be very difficult to scale back the enhanced monitoring that civilians now have. There has been a huge surge in digital surveillance, world over. Governments are employing vast programmes for mobile data tracking, recoding individuals personal contact with others. There is research going into whether drones could be employed to sail over our heads to monitor and enforce social isolation regimes. CCTV with facial recognition – ever more prevalent.

In Moscow, its citizens are required to have a QR code issued to them to be allowed to travel on its streets. In China hundreds of millions of people installed mandatory 'health code' apps. India are experimenting with mobile tracking apps with geolocated selfies. And this is just the beginning. The possibilities for this power to be grossly abused is endless.

I am sorry if I have laboured the point somewhat, but if you have got this far, then I thank you for hearing me out. And if you have got this far and share my concerns then I urge you to join our movement.

We have cells in every major city in the UK – and most towns. And our discussion forum here on the dark net has grown to an incredible 30,000 plus strong. And it's growing. Make no mistake, this will not be for the faint-hearted. Fighting for civil liberties never has been, all through the ages. This is warfare. And very soon, we will strike harder, and on a bigger scale than they can imagine.

If you are reading this and you want to take up this fight, then please make yourself known. I require you to register a handle here, and directly contact me. I need your name, IP address, precise location and national insurance number.

I also need you to buy a burner phone. If you intend on being a highly committed activist, you may need a few.

I have been lucky enough to initially work with several key individuals in Liverpool, where we took some initial affirmative action at the start of April, setting fire to a 5G mast in the city centre. The fires are not reckless, and do not pose a risk to human life. Firefighters can get them under control swiftly, but it gives us enough time to allow the fire to melt the circuitry.

We quickly gained some associates in Birmingham next, and then Belfast, and the individuals running these tac teams are key to the growth and organisation of our events. They will co-ordinate small teams from the successfully vetted applicant – sometimes the missions are solo missions. We will keep to these principles – which means that the more comrades that join us, we will have a wider spread to co-ordinate multi target assaults at one time. We started with one or two per week, but last month – our third complete month – we completed over 100 disablements. We will continue at this rate – not sparing any tower. 2G, 3G or 4G included. They are all part of the problem.

If we do not accept you as a comrade, please do not be offended. This is to preserve the integrity of the body. We do in depth background checks, and if there is some association in your past, for example, that red flags your profile - you will not be accepted, and subsequently blocked. We also have a policy of random blocking. Do not let this deter you though. If you are a committed believer, there is still lots you can do to help our cause. This can be as simple as stepping in and defending the actions on social media message boards, or even calling a phone in and presenting our side of the argument (we would recommend that you use aliases and fake profiles when carrying out any of the above). All this is important work and vital to our crusade.

We strictly do not advocate violence to any utilities workers who may be in the vicinity, or approach you – unless, of course – actions are required to defend yourselves. Equally we do not seek to harass any workers. As well as not being viewed sympathetically by the world at large, we already have several employees of the major telecoms' operators working with us. You can appreciate how important their involvement is, and how this key relationship could be soured if hostility were shown to any of their colleagues. In fact – it is a key condition of their involvement. Any member breaching this will face the consequences and, whilst I do not intend to issue threats, I will advise that there will be a heavy price for such treasonous behaviour. We have the technological know-how to fundamentally alter personal records, effectively meaning that we can re-write anyone's history - to reflect anything we wish. No matter how damning.

But we must not dwell on this. We are on the cusp of an exciting time. For us, for the environment, for the animal kingdom, and ultimately for all humanity. We are on the brink of something great.

You will have noticed a stopwatch counting down from 44 minutes in the bottom right corner of the screen. It begins when I make the post, and when the time expires, the post is automatically deleted. If you want to be a part of the solution and not the problem, then register below and you will be contacted via a secure link. Remember…\<disconnected\>….\<reload\>

404 error
This page doesn't exist

The Thing About Paranoia

<u>April 20th, 2020</u>

I'm going to hide this message when I'm finished. Then if I don't make it there will be some kind of record. The virus has been hitting us particularly hard now for 48 hours.

I haven't been outside my room for ten days, and nobody has crossed the threshold to come inside. I'm one of the lucky ones. I can do most things myself.

There was about 75 people living in this care home when I moved in a few months ago. All older, like myself, many of them suffered with dementia, or had other physical impairments that meant they required support within a residential environment.

In the last six weeks, that number had reduced by 15 residents. All taken by the virus, which had somehow breached our defence and was now living amongst us. It had spread like invisible wildfire.

Emergency action was taken. No visitors, no family. Strict procedures. Staff had to shower between each one to one interaction with the residents. The communal areas (the lounge, the café) closed. Solitary lockdown - more or less. Thirty minutes allowed in the patio area per day, if requested.

I decided to only receive in one evening meal per day. Each meal is brought by whatever member of staff is on the shift, so I thought that if I cut down the amount of meals that I have in a day to a third of the usual amount, then it's another huge risk reduction. I have things to snack on in my room anyway, on account of some supplies my son brought me. I have muesli bars, crackers, nuts – enough to keep me going until tea-time. Fortunately, I don't have a big appetite these days anyway.

All the staff have complied with my wishes. Frankly, I think they have enough on their plate to be getting on with, without arguing the toss with me about my dietary requirements. They know that if I need something, I am compos mentis and capable of asking for it. I receive my specialist medicine on a weekly basis. Overall, I am highly self-sufficient, and as I say, they are probably glad.

There's one care worker that I'm not keen on. Carl - a tall chap, thick Brummie accent. He always makes a fuss; over the top; I feel as though he speaks to me like a simpleton. I don't like it when he drops off my evening meal. I get him every few nights, and he always makes me anxious – he brought it last night.

There was a knock on the door earlier on, as usual. It always takes me a minute to get up out of the chair, grab my Zimmer frame and steady myself before I shuffle over to the door. I usually call out that I am on my way, and to request that they place the tray on the small coffee table in the corridor, next to my door.

Most respond with an 'ok' or 'no problem', but when it's Carl he always says something like, 'It's ok', or 'I'll wait right here.' I open the door a fraction to check who it is, and it's Carl.

I had repeated my request to place it on the table and retreat, but he just stood there holding the tray instead. His stare fixed on me.

"Now there's no need for that Eric. Come on, you just go back in sit down, and I'll bring it in for you," he said - using a voice that you would use to persuade a child to eat their broccoli.

"Carl, as I said before, please just put it on the coffee table as I have agreed with the rest of your team and managers."

He had a disposable type face mask on, but I can tell from the lines on his eyes he is flashing a big toothy smile underneath it. His eyes wide, as usual, teetering on the point of what I would describe as a crazed expression. I could sense the internal dialogue going on inside him – giving him this overall air of unpredictability.

"Eric now don't be silly. You go in and sit down, and I'll bring your tray in and I'll be off. It's perfectly safe. There's nothing wrong with me."

"Really Carl, please place it on the table and when you've gone back up the hall, I will collect it and bring it in. I'm isolating."

"Eric, I'm your carer, and your friend. If you can't trust me, who can you trust?"

"Carl – my mind is made up. Please."

Still clearly beaming, he shook his head from side to side in an exaggerated, exasperated fashion and let out a big, patronising sigh.

"Well, if you're going to fuss, then I will, but you need to promise me you are going to finish it all. You're not eating enough. You need your strength."

"Thank you, Carl. Of course," I asserted.

Carl put the tray on the table, and slowly backed down the hall. No sooner had I backed up my frame to fully open the door, he had turned around and was back a few inches from the door frame.

"Oh, that's right, your son called earlier."

"Carl – please, back up."

Carl looked sheepish. "I'm sorry, I'm sorry, just thought you would like to know. He said he will try you again tomorrow on your mobile," and then wagging his finger at me, "now don't forget to charge it tonight!"

"Thank you, I will, now if you please." Carl had nodded and walked off up the corridor, as I gathered the tray, shut, and locked the door and beat a hasty retreat to my table.

This was a typical encounter with him. I cannot believe that somebody could be so obstinate despite an individual's distinct wishes. I felt this type of behaviour suspicious, but I am not sure of a motive at this time – if any of course. It just feels odd.

Maybe he is just a well-meaning, if not slightly irritating, member of staff trying to do his best. Or maybe he is a virus carrying menace – full of sick intent to infect those he had been entrusted to care for. Revenge, perhaps, for years of emptying bedpans and talking orders. An angel of death. A killer who would never leave a weapon, or a crime scene. Who would never have to answer to a potential compendium of carnage.

I had read about that sort of thing before. Carriers of the HIV virus, wilfully engaging in sexual acts with others, knowing that there would be a strong chance of passing the infection on. People had been incarcerated for it. That required so much more overt interaction though.

"Listen to yourself!" I have literally just exclaimed out loud as I even write.

Perhaps the isolation is getting to me. I will continue recording my thoughts tomorrow.

That was enough writing for one day. I would carry on tomorrow. I want to document how this all plays out. My memory isn't so great anymore, although I'm grateful it's not as bad as some people here. I haven't seen my son and his family for almost five weeks now, since the care home banned all visitors and I am afraid if I don't write everything down, I could forget to tell him something. Something important, or that could help.

Time for bed for now. What did I have to do before bed? It escapes me now. It can't have been important.

April 22nd, 2020

Since I last wrote, we have lost four more residents.

I know when something is happening. From my window at the front, on the roadside, I can see the ambulances pull up. No sirens, sometimes lights. Sometimes this is followed by lots of movement and voices outside in the corridor if it's one of the neighbours on my floor. It is normally between 20 and 30 minutes before I see the ambulance crew then return to their vehicle with their patient.

On each occasion they have been this week, the body has been motionless with a blanket covering the face as it is effortlessly slid into the back of the ambulance. It is interesting that when your time is up, the last few journeys your physical being takes tends to be consistently performed with this continuous, uninterrupted smooth movement.

Slide into the back the ambulance.

Slide into the mortuary cabinet.

Slide into the oven at the crematorium.

And just like a helter-skelter, the ride is over.

One of the carers got a confirmed case of it this week too. I liked her too, she was very efficient. When she was on duty everything ran like clockwork. Everything was on time. I'm sure she'll be ok. She's only in her thirties, and I know she likes to exercise and keep fit. Sometimes I can see her leaving work in her running attire. It's getting the replacement people in that worries me.

I still haven't managed to catch up with my son yet. I know he has rung the main reception again, but we cannot have multiple people using a phone. Plus - I would refuse to leave my room anyway. I think he tried asking the carers to physically help me charge my phone, but they know I won't allow anyone in and much less handle my possessions.

I had wanted to charge my phone last night, but I must have misplaced my charger. I only have a modest sized room and a small amount of worldly possessions, but I just cannot find it anywhere. Nobody has been in, of course, so I am sure I must have just put it somewhere so safe that I cannot find it myself! It will no doubt turn up. Hopefully soon – I would dearly love to speak to my two grandchildren. Rosie and the younger one.

I don't mind admitting, I am scared. Very scared. It appears the virus is winning, and that our defences are becoming ever more breached. I can see that it was advancing on us. And I have some pedigree in reaching this decision.

I was trained to spot the trends of warfare when I did my training with the Royal Artillery Signals unit. This enabled me to become an observation post signaller in World War II – including at the D-Day landings. I would be right in the thick of things, just behind the front line. I was armed, but this was really for emergency usage. My job was to observe the ebb and the flow of battles, and to make the calls on where we should focus the attack. I'd then communicate – either in Morse code, or over the radio – to the battery and the regiment where to fire the guns. I can remember this like it was yesterday.

I regularly marvel at the similarity with what I am facing now. Here I am again, slightly behind the front line, but nonetheless in the thick of things. I am not armed at all this time, neither do I have any back up to communicate a plan to. We are on the back foot and the enemy is not retreating. I hope I am not simply observing our demise this time.

April 25th, 2020

I write this at just after ten pm. It has been a terrifying day. Six more went just today alone. That to add to the two from yesterday.

The voices in the corridors belong to mainly strangers now. I don't recognise the pitch or tones of most of them. Two more of the care team developed symptoms and were sent home. I understand they recruited some temporary staff – may even be volunteers. I can hear a distinct lack of control in the corridors - a result of the lack of experience out there amongst them. A lack of experience with death, especially. Whenever we have an incident, I can feel the tension and the panic from my room. I can hear the fear and distress in their voices. They seem to be barely keeping it together.

I surface only briefly for my evening meal and medication. Opening the door just long enough and wide enough to be able to retrieve the tray and get back inside as soon as possible. The rest of the day, I sit in my old yellow armchair next to my bed, trying to stay alert and read the situation, just like I did when I was at my post in Normandy.

I listen intently to the comings and goings and try to monitor what is happening. It is ultimately futile, as I cannot leave my room, nor could I do anything to assist or defend myself if the dreaded enemy eventually invaded my space. Perhaps I am waiting for all the noise to one day be replaced with the entire building falling still; until only I will remain here. The question of how I get out would remain. Walking the corridors and touching the hard surfaces could leave me open to picking up the infection myself. I am on the second storey, so I can't get out any other way....

I have decided that, if it comes to this, I will hold my position for no less than three days. After three days of confirmed silence, I would attempt to walk out of here through the visitors' entrance at the front. My only obstacle is sustaining myself during this time. My snack supplies have seriously diminished in the last few weeks, and I am

126

finding that I am very hungry by the time my tea comes around.

Carl brings it most evenings now. I'm starting to think that he is tormenting me now. What other reason could there be for his total disregard of my polite, and sensible, requests. He constantly tries to hand it to me, laughs off my prescribed cautious approach. I can't think why. My way is quicker and there must be plenty of work to be getting on with. Having said that, he has a decreasing amount of people to look after every day, and since the lockdown there aren't any care homes accepting in new residents. In fact, we must be rapidly approaching 50% capacity.

I have become aware that the complete lack of interaction with anybody – over and above five minutes a day - is having a detrimental effect on my mental well-being. This sounds most unusual, but I worry about how I would perform in the throes of an actual conversation. I wonder if I would be able to follow the protocols and etiquette anymore. Writing things down is the only way I can both express and articulate myself in a way that makes sense. Even these entries can take a day to perfect. There are lots of failed drafts before I put together my final draft. Paragraph by paragraph. I persevere with it most days as in some ways the focus keeps me going, but some days it is too much for me.

I used to think that I was one of the lucky one, but I am starting to think that perhaps the residents with the more serious memory issues than my own have been spared in some way from the constant fear and tension that I live with. Or perhaps the repeated comprehension and subsequent erasure from their mind is even more torturous. Reliving the news every day. I can't imagine the horrible confusion they would endure either way. The mind truly is a prison.

April 26th, 2020

Three more dead this morning.

Carl attempted to open my door and enter the room to hand me my dinner today. When I heard the turn of the lock, I shouted blue murder at the intruder to stay outside. I think the shock made him stop dead in his tracks.

When I eventually got to the door, he was still just sheepishly smiling as though I had caught him with his hand in the cookie jar, although he had placed the tray down. I didn't return his greeting. I indignantly picked up the tray and returned inside instead.

I still can't find my phone charger. It doesn't make sense. There is nowhere left to look.

April 28th, 2020

Six more dead. The halls outside are like the Marie Celeste. Deserted, and mostly silent.

I occasionally hear noise coming from the lower floor, just some bumping and doors closing. Beds and other pieces of furniture being dragged along the floor.

Very little movement outside too. No noise, or murmur, or rustle. The occasional car passing on the main road several hundred yards away was all. It was a beautiful day, but even the sunlight streaming through my window somehow feels cold.

As the silence presses in on me, the only noise that remains constant is the beating of my own heart. Which is somewhat comforting at least.

May 2nd, 2020

I don't know how many more deaths there have been in the last few days. I somehow lost my pen, to record it and I cannot remember.

Only this morning, whilst looking for the last of my crackers, I came across a crossword book my son had originally brought me when I moved in here. It had a small biro sellotaped to the front, the type they give you at a bookmaker's office.

I hadn't needed it at first. I had my own Mont Blanc pen. My son bought it for me as a retirement gift years ago. Everyone had always admired it, all the staff and residents alike.

I have been having more dark thoughts today. The phone charger is gone, and I am seriously concerned that I may never speak to my family ever again.

May 4th, 2020

Eight more. This is catastrophic.

I am finding I don't have the concentration to write much anymore. A few sentences can take hours to produce.

It is very still and calm on my landing. This is how I've heard the eye of a storm being described more than once. If it weren't for the appearance of my evening meal - brought

---

I must've nodded off. Normally have an afternoon nap, but what has woken me up?

I'm still a bit bleary eyed. I'll blink a few times, gently rub me eyes. Bit blurry but getting better.

There's someone in my room.

I give my eyes another rub. There is someone standing four feet in front of me, looming over me. A tall dark figure.

I still can't make out who it is, they have a hooded robe on. New PPE, no doubt. Something in their left hand catches the light, and it looks as though they are holding an hourglass. In their other hand, perhaps an upside-down broom with something shiny and silver attached to where the bristles would be.

They speak to me; I recognise the voice. "It's ok Eric, relax. I just brought you a drink, thought you could use it."

It's Carl.

I ask him why he has come in my room, but he doesn't answer me, he just smirks. I see this smile now as he is not wearing his face mask, or indeed any of his usual uniform.

"You should trust me Eric, I was here to help you."

Despite pleading not to come closer he approached and sat on the corner of my bed, adjacent to my armchair where I had taken a nap.

My clear vision had returned, and I could see it wasn't an hourglass, but a whiskey glass he was holding. Two in fact. He set them both down on the table, next to my chess board and produced a small bottle of scotch from his pocket. He poured us one each and handed it to me.

Frightened, I accepted the glass from him, hoping that my subservience may placate him, and make him think twice about doing whatever he had in mind. I raise the glass to my mouth at the same time Carl does. We stare each other right in the eyes, and he pauses, waiting until I sip the scotch before he takes his swig.

I ask him if he plays chess.

"I guess I'll be learning."

As he reaches across to lay the board out, he coughs.

Dopamine Fingertips

Ian Rush, John Barnes, Kenny Dalglish, Bruce Grobbelaar, Alan Hansen.

That's an easy one – post.

No, no, no, delete. They can't all be Liverpool players from the same era.

Definitely Rush and Dalglish. Could probably lose Barnes. Need some European players in there so I can show my knowledge of the game. Holland were a force in the late eighties.

Ruud Gullit! Now there's a player. What a barnet on him too. Oh, and Marco Van Basten. I'll put Grobbelaar back in the 'maybe' pile for a minute. Now, does Hansen deserve that last spot? Then it would be three Liverpool players, and two Dutch players. Probably need to give a nod to another UK player – just to show I'm fair minded, and not completely biased. Not a Manc though – no chance. When did Le Tissier's career really take off? I'd have to look that one up. He'd be a good one to include.

So that's four 'definitelys' on my list. Hmmm. Finding five players that made me fall in love with football to post on Facebook is harder than I thought. I'll scroll through my news feed and look at what other people have posted while I have my morning coffee. No-one will notice if I only nick one. Someone else could even pop into my head.

These Boris Johnsons memes are a bit boring now.

Haha – I can watch those dancing funeral guys over and over.

Why are there so many ads on here for lots of cheap Chinese-made tech lately?

Fair play, he's done a nice job of his garden.

How on earth can there possibly be 62 photos of your garden VE party worth sharing? I'll just take a quick look through a few of them to find out.

I don't get that joke. Having said that, it has got over 100k likes. I'll have to let that one slide. I'm not asking to have it explained to me. I might even share it.

Oh, I don't fucking know what two red apples plus three brooms plus a witch adds up too!

I think it's 35 though.

I'll just scroll through the results to check. Hmm, she's saying that's wrong, but it can't be.

A notification. Someone's tagged me. The 10 most influential movies of my life? That reminds me – I still need to do the 10 albums that shaped my life. I still haven't completely distilled my shortlist down from twenty to ten. Grrrrr. I've got six 'definitelys' and the last four could literally be any of the remaining fourteen. It's going to be enjoyable sorting that little lot out!

I'll start giving it some thought while I am making my lunch – I didn't realise that was the time! It's weird although I'm often posting about being bored, I'm actually not, and time seems to be going by faster than usual! Not long and I can crack open my first craft ale of the day. I think I'll go for that fruity little number from the small brewery in Brazil. Overtones of elderberry and fruits of the forest apparently. Got it from a new craft beer club I signed up too. First order was just a fiver for ten craft ales from all over the world. Must remember to cancel that though – goes up to twenty quid a week after that for the same amount of beer.

I'll just have a glass of Coke with my lunch I think......OMG.... that is the most perfect fried egg on toast I have ever seen in my life. Where's my camera?

Posted.

Bugger – you can see where the fat has spat out of the pan on to the surface in that photo. It's not too bad. I'll clean it up later. I'll use the rest of that bleach I diluted with water in the glass. Great 'life hack' that was for when you run out of antibacterial spray. Better than the real thing, though I probably used a bit too much bleach! I knew following that Facebook page would pay off one day.

I don't know where to start with movies. So, if I think back to my favourite movies as a kid that I watched a hundred times. Goonies. That's a good starting point. And the Breakfast Club, and The Lost Boys. This is easier than I thought.

Um.

I think I'll just Google "classic 80's movies".

First one - Ferris Bueller's Day Off! Of course, can't miss that one off.

Wow – Back to the Future, Ghostbusters, Indiana Jones, Top Gun, Stand By Me, ET – nah fuck ET, take it off. The Princess Bride, Gremlins, The Terminator, Die Hard. STAR WARS. Christ, that's just made matters worse – there's too many to choose from. Close that screen down. I'll stick with Goonies, The Breakfast Club and The Lost Boys for now.

Actually, I'll take the option of posting one a day instead of all at once. I can think about it properly then. That will give me time to do my top ten albums too. I'm a bit concerned that people might think that some of my album choices are shit. No – it'll be ok. I don't have to justify the choices – it actually stipulates 'no explanation, no words'. Or I could just choose albums by Bob Dylan and The Beatles even though I never listen to them – lol! Wow, that egg tasted as good as it looked. 18 likes?? Well I suppose I only posted it twenty minutes ago.

I might actually watch the Prime Ministers press briefing later today. See how much longer we will have of this lockdown. It's been almost seven weeks already. I still haven't even made a start on learning French – or painting my flat. Well they say this could be going on until October, so no hurry.

Was that my WhatsApp notification? Yes, it was.

Oh God – it's from Tony King! Why am I turning the volume down – it's only me here. I better had anyway. The window is open.

Ha! Superb. It's a video of Donald Trump singing REM's 'Losing My Religion' – only the words have been changed and it's called 'Losing My Civilians' - but it's all dubbed in Trumps voice! Brilliant. What REM album was that off? That could be a good one to include in my top ten albums. Have a quick scroll, then I might do those dishes.

Wind your neck in. 5k is nothing. Even I've done a 5k run before.

Is that a hot tub in his garden? Let me zoom in. It is. I didn't know he had one of those!

Yeah, yeah, the first few Joe Exotic costumes I saw were quite funny. Come on be original.

Have these people seriously just heard of Tik Tok? My little sister has been on it for over a year.

Jesus Christ – he made 32 mil in the end. Just for walking around his garden.

Is it legal to rip off designer aftershaves and then advertise them as copies? It's all about the bottle for me. There's a thought - I could buy an original and then just refill it with the copy.

Hang on. What's he doing there? 'My life for a week'. Take a photo each day in black and white, with no words. I haven't been tagged in that one. I could go and take some really arty photos on the common. I could do some of me looking really moody and mysterious. My shirt off, looking wistfully into the distance. I'm going to ask Tammy to nominate me.

Oh no, it's the daily briefing in half an hour and I haven't even thought of one more movie or album to include in my list. I promised myself that today I would finish the football player and top albums lists. I was nominated for the football player and albums list over a week ago. I was only nominated for choosing the ten video games that shaped my taste in games over the years two days ago, so I won't panic over that one. I already have five. Six if you include Shinobi, if I need it. Seven with Golden Axe!

Oh wow, that robin red breast has wandered right on to my windowsill. Where's my camera? Slowly, slowly. Ok, hold still – YESS. I bet that will look amazing with the beauty filter. Class that.

"Thank you for coming to pay me a visit Mr Robin. #missingnature #2mrule #protectiveglassscreen #firstlockdownvisitor #rockyrobin <heart> "

Post. Superb. That's a bonus post for today, I thought I was going to struggle for content. I can take it easy tonight now. Actually, shit, I should have kept that for the 'my life' challenge. Bollocks, it's been liked already. Oh well, leave it up.

While I'm here, I'll check my notifications. Tammy still hasn't nominated me yet. I sent it over ten minutes ago. Why hasn't she done it? Not like she's busy or anything is it. Bit selfish if you ask me. She's been a bit funny lately mind. Taking ages to come back to me. And she shared one of those mental health posts about how great it is to be asked if you're ok? And another about 'having to review her circle when this is over'. I don't think she means me. Can she? I'll send her the funny video of that talking dog just in case.

What shall I binge watch on Netflix tonight? No point asking my Facebook friends, I've already seen everything they suggest! Tiger King. Ozarks. You. Hollywood? Hmm not seen that one. Oh yes, I did. It's hard to remember the ins and outs of most of these shows with my phone buzzing away on the table next to me. Get so easily distracted.

The daily briefing has started.

.

.

.

.

I'm bored with this now. Every time they speak it seems to start with 'and we've been really clear on this point' but it's not clear to me. I'll just wait for my boss to ring me and tell me what's happening when the time comes. And if I'm not ready to go back I'll just have to tell him my temperature is too high, or I've started coughing. Try and milk it as much as I can. They try and squeeze as much out of me as they can – well the boots on the other foot now. It's only fair.

I was thinking about getting another job anyway – don't want to be a production operative in a washing line factory all my life. One of the blokes in accounts told me they have almost run out of money anyway and won't be there much longer. They'd be better off growing cannabis plants there, instead of making washing lines imo – lol.

If I'm being honest with myself, I only really wanted to watch the daily briefing to find out when Maccy D's are back open. Ha-ha. God, I could smash three 'Big Tastys' now – and still have room for an Oreo McFlurry!

It must be time for tea. Let's see what's on the menu tonight.

Tinned chicken meatballs in gravy. Tinned chilli con carne. Tinned chicken curry – extra hot. Tinned chicken pie. Don't really like any of them. Not a lot left in my cupboards. Need some shopping. Mum brought me bagfulls of stuff in the middle of March. There was so much food, and cleaning stuff, I had to stack it on my bistro table and eat off a tray instead. She's been shielding ever since because of a recent operation she had, and my supplies are dwindling. I had better think about going out and picking some things up for myself soon. Might do me some good to go for a walk. Probably a good idea to get some fresh air after all this time. Or maybe I'll use that click and collect service that the supermarkets do. I'll lie about my age – or maybe say it's for my Mother so they prioritise my order - lol.

Tea for tonight is looking grim though. Haven't even got any beans for some beans on toast. What's that behind the rice pudding at the back? Ah-ha – a Pot Noodle. And not just any old Pot Noodle – the 'Bombay Bad Boy'. Situation resolved! Result.

While the kettle's boiling I'll have a look if Tammy's seen my video.

Well she's seen it – five minutes ago – but she's not replied. This is serious. I'll send her some heart and cuddling emojis.

I enjoyed that documentary I watched the other day. It makes so much sense to say that emojis are the hieroglyphics of their day. I can't believe the guy talking thought that emojis are less complex that basic Egyptian drawings though. Idiot.

Still nothing from Tammy. She has seen the emojis though.

I know what will cheer her up. I haven't done my neck and nominate challenge! Should I do it? It's not very classy. Go on I will, what the hell. I still have that Jägermeister in my top cupboard from Seren's birthday night out. That was a top night out. Best pre drinks party I've ever had in my bedsit.

There it is. Half a bottle still left. It'll have to be a pretty impressive measure. That's roughly four shots in there. Bit more. Wow. This is going to be rough. Just need to set up my camera to film.

"Hi Guys. Hope you are all okay out there in these crazy, crazy times. I'm hopefully going to cheer you up with my neck and nominate challenge – thanks to Samir for the nomination. Sending love, sunshine, and a nomination to my bestie Tammy. Be kind and bottoms up."

.

JESUS CHRIST. I'm retching. I'm going to be violently ill. Stop the camera.

I can't spit this bile out quick enough. My mouth keeps filling up again.

GOD. I'm going to be sick.

.

Some splattered on me. Still swallowing hard to get rid of the bile. It's even coming out of my eyes. Everything's blurry. EUURRGHHHH.

I need a drink. Quickly. That'll do. Got to get rid of this taste. Keep drinking.

Downed it. That a little better – can't taste the Jaeger anymore. But, wait…

What was that? It didn't taste right. That wasn't a glass of water.

Oh fuck, no. Fuck no. That was the…...

OH FUCK - NO. I can't of. Oh fuck. Get to the toilet. Fuck. Fingers down the throat, spew it back up quick. Oh fuck.

<BLEURGH>

I need to ring an ambulance.

<BLEURGH>

FUCK!!! My phones just died.

<BLEURGH>

Be calm. Be calm. I'll be ok. I'll be ok. I'm not gonna die.

Donald Trump said it was ok, didn't he?

Blood Of The Wicked

The team were so frustrated. It seemed as though we had gotten so close to finally solving it this time. But as the pandemic began taking off, our workload took us into different directions – public order stuff mainly.

And then I had caught a dose of it and wound up here in St Bart's - on a ventilator at its worst, but back on a ward with other patients now. I had felt like death for a week but (hopefully) I was now on the mend. It had been a scary time as I was in the vulnerable group because of my advancing years! It was the longest I had gone apart from my wife since we met - thirty-five years ago. I had facetimed her a few times, and had spoken to my nephew once, but apart from this, I had time to kill. So, it was only natural, that as I lay there in my hospital bed, I would wind up doing an awful lot of thinking.

For five years and three months I had been chief investigating officer on the case. Over five years of chasing shadows, following up on leads that had never gone anywhere and endless paperwork and media engagements.

It was a high-profile case, and as such had garnered lots of column inches. This was partly down to the fact that the victim had been something of a reality TV celebrity – albeit a very minor one – and partly because the circumstances of her murder fell into the realm of being not just creepy, but extremely chilling. The twisted events that took place put many fictionalised horror stories in the shade, and the media did an incredible of capitalising on this and sensationalising every detail and aspect of the subsequent investigation as possible.

As a result, all types of media organisations were constantly placing demands upon our time for updates, or just asking us to confirm more salacious details. The high level of publicity in turn meant that our department also received around five times more phone-calls from the general public than a typical murder case – many suggesting potential suspects' names to us, and many just submitting their outlandish, baseless theories.

Of course, we had to follow up the vast majority of these in the interests of leaving no stone unturned. Although we could prioritise the investigation of the individuals who had been named or suggested more than once, we could not completely dismiss anyone. It would leave us open to huge criticism if it transpired that we had dismissed a name that later proved to be the culprit – particularly if he or she struck again before we could apprehend them.

The pressure this put on our resources was immense and had a huge impact in terms of our ability to solve the case. Despite the many added pressures this case provided us with, we still only had a small team assigned to it, which further dwindled as time went on due to the cuts the government had made in front line policing combined with the re-allocation of our resource to help address the huge explosion in knife crime - particularly here in London.

It had seemed as though I had spent more time going through the motions of following up weak leads and giving interviews and talking to the media than carrying out a meaningful investigation. There are occasions – when you are geared up sufficiently – where it accelerates the progress of an investigation to have a case in the public eye. For example, if you are trying to piece together a suspects' movements and can appeal for eye witnesses that may have been in a public area at the time to report anything they may have seen in, the leads you receive inward can help to build a picture up of the events, and assist in making charges. With the incredible amount of surveillance equipment and camera phones in use by the general public, appealing for footage from people's personal devices, dash-cams etc has also proven exceptionally helpful in getting prosecutions. In both cases, exceptional levels of press coverage push the investigation forward – as a rule of thumb.

Applied to a case like this, it only served as a distraction. The incident occurred at a remote private residence. The opportunity for any eyewitnesses to come forward or for any recorded footage to materialise was minimal, compared to the same event occurring in a build-up residential area near a large town or city. When coupled with the celebrity profile of the victim and the lack of genuine intelligence, we simply ended up in a position where rampant speculation overshadowed any progress we were making. It was a frustrating time for my team and I, and we were all burdened with the guilt of not being able to offer the family any justice, and thus closure on this terrible affair.

On the night of February 9th, 2015, along with her Mother and Father, Stella Shaw – most famous for starring in 'Celebrity Sex on the Beach' - was brutally murdered at her parents' home on the fringes of a small chocolate-box type village in Surrey.

Stella's budding television career had begun with a recurring role in the reality show 'REAL Surrey Socialites'. Roy Shaw, her Father, had built up a financially successful building contractors from scratch thirty years previous. He had made a number of enemies on this journey and was no stranger to a courtroom in regard to some 'outstanding business matters' he had appeared reluctant to settle.

Childhood sweethearts, he had been married to her Mother, Sonia, since their early twenties. The wealth that he had accumulated through his endeavours had ensured that his family enjoyed the very best things in life – be it holidays, cars, or other material possessions. It was this lifestyle that had opened doors for Stella and presented the opportunity for her to join the cast of this show in the third season. As a 'face' on the Surrey VIP scene, she was exactly the kind of person whose life the show sought to glorify and fetishize. Despite their wealth - and the potential of jealousy amongst other people who may have felt they had flaunted it - they remained mostly well liked within their community.

This new found fame allowed Stella to embark upon what had become a fairly well trodden path of reality TV star growing their own personal 'brand' and transitioning to general media 'personality', social media influencer and all round high street clothes horse and nightclub opener. After a few years plying these trades, she landed her biggest gig to date in the aforementioned 'Celebrity Sex on the Beach' programme. This enjoyed a prime-time late evening slot on the broadcaster's principal channel, every day, for around six weeks.

Stella had made quite an impact on the show and had lasted until the final episode before being voted off (the exact mechanics of how this occurs alludes me). During the course of the show she had been involved in several furious disputes with other contestants – male and female – and had gained the (dubious) honour of spending the most time in the 'Sandy Sex Shack' with several fellow contestants, again – of both sexes. One tabloid had spitefully dubbed her as the 'Beach Hut Slut' in their crass reports of each episode – prior to her murder, of course.

On the night in question, the family had earlier that evening been dining at a local speciality fish restaurant a few miles down the road with another family that lived relatively nearby. Testimonies from the staff at the restaurant, as well as their friends told us that they had arrived at just before 7pm. They had enjoyed a glass of wine at the bar, before being sat at their table around 45 minutes later when their friends had arrived. They were regulars at the restaurant, and the barman who had served and chatted with them had been a school mate of Stella's. His name was Patrick Pierce, and he had told investigators that there was nothing unusual about their behaviour. They seemed perfectly relaxed on the night in question and had enjoyed a twenty minute or so conversation with him about general topics. There was no evidence of any tension or anxieties present amongst them and nothing had stood out as different from all the other occasions when they had followed a very similar dining routine. All these key players had been thoroughly background checked. Patrick had been cleared as a suspect very early on into the investigation. We had no reason to suspect he had a motive as well as having strong alibis both at work, at the petrol station he used on the way home that night, and also from his wife when he did arrive home.

The waiter that served them that night was a Daniel Popescu. When the Shaws friends had arrived, Mike and Julie Burke and their daughter Chelsea – Stella's best friend – he had seated them and looked after them for the rest of the evening. It was reported as being a relaxed, friendly, and informal occasion with lots of laughs coming from the table throughout the evening. From Daniels account – supported by analysing the bill   nobody had over indulged on alcohol and it was a perfectly civilised affair. For their mains, Stella had ordered the Sea Bass in a dark soy and ginger sauce and her parents had both opted for a hearty bowl of clam chowder packed with smoked bacon, shellfish potatoes and cream; a house specialty.

At around 9.30pm, Daniel was asked to call both families a taxi each to return to their respective homes. They had a final glass of wine at the bar area, once again chatting with Patrick, before their taxis arrived. They collected their coats from the cloakroom, thanked the staff, said their goodbyes, and left the restaurant to get into their taxis. The Shaws took the first taxi that came - probably on account of having the furthest distance to travel home – and minutes later the second taxi arrived, and the Burke family also departed.

The taxi driver, a local owner/driver called Steve Drinkwater, recalled dropping them home twenty minutes or so later – engaging them in the typical taxi driver patter that he did with most of his customers. As they approached the gates to the Shaws' recently converted barn conversion, Steve told how the automatic lights had flicked on, Roy had handed him a couple of notes and advised him to keep the change. He had mentioned how it was an underwhelming tip for a man of Roys apparent means, but he politely thanked him as they got out of his cab, and Steve pulled away and on to the next job.

Steve was the last known person to see any of them alive. Doctors later concluded that they were all bludgeoned to death with one of Roy Shaw's axes that he kept in his workshop, between the hours of approximately midnight and 5am.

The alarm was raised by one of Roy's business partners, Stephen 'Ashy' Ash, who arrived at the house early the next morning – around seven – to collect Roy so they could travel together to visit the site of a future job they were undertaking. Following attempts to wake Roy by firstly beeping the horn in his car from the driveway, and then by repeatedly knocking the front door, Ashy had gone around the back to see if he could see anyone outside. It was a beautiful, fresh morning, and sometimes the family took their morning coffee on the rear terrace.

Once around the back of the house, Ashy reported sensing that something was seriously wrong quite quickly. There was nobody about and the whole house was still and silent. When he approached the rear porch and saw that the door was unlocked, and ajar, his concern grew. He had described how he had decided to proceed quietly into the house rather than going in calling out loudly. As he entered the property through the back door, the poor light his eyes began adjusting to immediately highlighted the fact that all the curtains were closed. From his vantage point, he could see that the same was true of the adjoining downstairs rooms.

The kitchen had a large stone fireplace and Ashy had grabbed an ornamental poker that sat in its holder next to the hearth. Passing through the kitchen with increasing trepidation, he stated how he had firmly gripped the black iron poker with both hands and cocked it alongside his head; it was poised and ready to unload on any unwelcome intruder he would encounter.

Aside from the closed curtains, there was no other visual evidence that any wrong-doing was being concealed. Everything was reported as being neat and organised as usual, by Ashy, as he progressed through the house. He had stated that Sonia was extremely house-proud, and their home was always immaculate. He had noticed that nothing had been interfered with – suggesting that robbery was not the intention.

The bodies of Roy and Sonia Shaw were found lying naked from the waist up in their bed. The bedraggled sheets soaked in crimson. So much blood had been shed, that as Ashy took in the scene, he noticed a pool of blood had formed from a corner of the bed sheet where the saturated bed sheet had dripped on to the wooden flooring.

Sonia had always been an attractive woman and even in her advancing years was still very elegant and beautiful. Now, she lay in her bed with her head cracked open like a boiled egg – later to have been proven to have been bashed in with the blunt edge of the axe. She would be unrecognisable out of the context of her own bedroom; her face swollen with a black blotchy pattern across it where the stagnant blood had pooled – having succumbed to gravity now her heart had since stopped pumping blood. These patterns had helped us establish that the bodies had not been tampered with or moved since the murder and that they had been killed as they lay in their bed.

Roy's body was more exposed as the bed sheets had gathered up around his calf area. Also having suffered incredible damage to his head by a heavy instrument, he nonetheless had retained an element of expression. His face had been frozen into a wild-eyed stare. The surprise and horror of the attack was forever etched upon his face. Ashy later reported that – contrary to what he had seen in movies – the only discernible smell in the room was not from any level of decomposition, but the smell from where Ray had voided his bladder and bowels at the moment of death.

In his state of confusion and panic, Ashy had touched the by now cold corpse of Roy– vainly looking for a sign that his friends could be revived. Quickly realising that he could not, he retreated out of the room sobbing and – in a change of his previous strategy – ran across the upstairs landing shouting Stella's name. No answer ever came.

Stella was found in her own bedroom three doors along from her parents. Her corpse was slumped underneath the window, blood splattered all over her plush, ivory white, oak radiator cover. With traces of white paint underneath her fingernails, the forensics suggested that she had also been brutally beaten to death but this time from behind, as she had tried to flee from her assailant by feverishly attempting to open - and exit the house - via her window.

Alongside her body was a tall lamp that had been pulled over – probably the result of a futile attempt at putting up a barrier between her and her assailant. The murder weapon protruded from a wooden beam in the overhead rafters having had the sharp edge swung and embedded into it.

At this point, Ashys 'fight or flight' instinct had kicked in, and he ran back outside and raced to the front of the house and got back into his car. He screeched off up the road to a small layby, where he had parked up, got back out and phoned 999 – but not before violently spewing across the off-side rear wing of his new Jaguar.

When we listened to the transcript of the call, our experts were satisfied that Ashy had sounded genuine. As the first person on the scene, he had been thoroughly background checked and questioned, but he was provisionally cleared fairly quickly. It didn't stop some of the tabloids from dredging up some unfounded rumours and conjecture from his distant past, however, that did cause a serious amount of distress to him and his family – all in the pursuit of sensationalising and thus monetising their stories to the maximum level possible.

The crime scene quickly became something of a circus, with media trucks lining the hedgerows that flanked the single car lane that lead to their cottage. Reporters waited on the gates for comments or a little nugget of progress that they could break to their audience. I was the first person to make an official statement at the gates.

"We can confirm that last night, the family of Roy and Sonia Shaw, and their daughter – television personality – Stella Shaw, were murdered at their family home by an intruder. We are appealing for anyone who saw any of the family's movements – or any other activity at the premises from yesterday afternoon onwards to come forward with this information – no matter how significant it may seem. I would ask everyone to respect their extended family and friend's privacy at this time – whom our thoughts are with in light of this brutal and cowardly crime."

I didn't quite release everything that we knew at this time.

As well as identifying and obtaining the murder weapon, discovering the method of striking them with the blunt edge, establishing an approximate time of murder, and understanding where the murder had occurred, we had other details that we had decided not to release publicly as yet.

One of the forensic team had taken a dog into the house who was made familiar with the murder weapon. It didn't take too long for the sniffer dog to lead the team to the staircase that wound around and went up to the converted attic. He led them straight to a Velux window and had begun barking. A team on the ground following up on what had agitated the dog found two spent cigarettes amongst the ornamental stones.

It quickly became apparent that we could rule out an aggravated burglary that had gone too far. It was suggested that the Shaw's killer – or killers – had hidden patiently in the attic for a likely several hours, waiting, for the family to retire to bed and fall asleep. During this time, the person(s) smoked two cigarettes and flicked them out of the Velux window when spent. This would explain how the parents were found lying in bed, and how the likelihood was that this had disturbed Stella who had tried to escape and had offered a small level of resistance.

As I mentioned, the status of Stella meant that speculation was rife – all fuelled by the media. As well as many ex beaus doing what basically amounted to a well-paid kiss and tell interview – with added emotion – we had a hash-tag campaign (#justiceforStella), ridiculous theories and heartfelt celebrity Instagram tributes. It slowed us down, and we sweated in the heat of the publics gaze.

Most crimes stand a better chance of being solved – or significant events coming to light – in the early days. The longer it remains unsolved, the colder the trail becomes but in the early days we had no significant or promising leads.

It also turned out that Roy had amassed several enemies that could have perhaps resorted to physical means to resolve a dispute, but we struggled to find one with enough just cause to commit murder. Not over a botched orangery.

More interesting to me was his colourful past and his business dealings when he used to operate a security firm running some nightclub doors in London. He seemed to have had quite a fearsome reputation, as well as some dubious business connections linked to the criminal underworld. In 1989 – just before he left the security world behind – one of his nightclub contracts had an incident where a young lad lost his life. It was all brushed under the carpet, and the cause of death was eventually given as death by misadventure; the lad was adjudged to have fallen down the fire escape steps from the top floor – landing on his head. The poor lad was from a one parent family. Lived on a council estate in Croydon with his mother. She was a prostitute. Had a bit of an arrest sheet with the Yard. He had no voice. No access to proper justice.

No matter how we sliced it though, all roads seemed to lead back to how Roy Shaw had conducted himself, and who he had upset....

My wife would go mad if she knew that this case was consuming me still whilst I was supposed to be recovering from something which could have easily taken my life; made me a statistic.

Not only was I in the vulnerable category because of my age, it was said that smokers were at a greater risk than non-smokers and, truth be told, I did enjoy a couple of cigarettes in certain circumstances – unbeknownst to her.

But I would have to live with her ire. I was now going to solve the case – on my terms, and before it was too late. Although compellingly frightening, coming to this realisation had been liberating for me. I knew that this tale must have its ending written, rather than continuing to tell the story when there is nothing meaningful left to say. I felt the freedom wash over me like a warm rain shower, breaking up the dark thunderclouds of an uncomfortably humid day.

I sat up and reached for my iPad and began typing out an email.

As I type, I am transported back to their attic; listening and waiting for the sound of the barrel in the lock to turn. I feel the crystallised burden and pain beginning to fragment within my soul.

As I think on, I remember looking down at this overweight fuckpig of a wannabe gangster defecating himself as he stares into my eyes knowing that I am now his God. I feel the fragments of this dark secret loosening up and drifting away.

And I allow myself to revel in it one more time before banishing the image from my mind forever. The image of me taking his slut of a daughter from him, just like the way he so callously took a son from me.

I want this.

I want my moment.

I want people to know.

I want Harry to know that I didn't let him get away with it after all.

And then I want to join him.

Such Sweet Sorrow

My apartment overlooks a small marina, maybe 100 boats. Nothing too massive like you would see in Puerto Banus, or Marbella. They tend to be owned and run by enthusiasts who live locally and use them at the weekend during the summer. Mostly sailing boats, though several power boats too. From talking to people who enjoy the pastime, it's quite simple to get involved, I think. You go to a local college and do an evening 'Yacht Master' class and I believe you're good to go. I don't think there's an exam at the end either (I'm not even sure its mandatory!) – I think you pretty much just need to turn up to pass the course. I suppose your subsequent success as a 'Captain' then determines on how seriously you took it.

The busiest day is a Sunday. This is when the most boats go out under the bascule bridge, and into the channel. I could watch the bridge move up and down all day. As a feat of engineering, I think it's incredible. It forms part of a path running from the marina, about 3km along the coastline, and into the city. With each side weighing almost 90 tonnes, it is manually operated on demand as boats need to pass through from the marina on to the channel. It raises up so high, that it can let boats out at any stage of the tide.

If you carry on across the bridge, and toward the city, in the Summer they often set a fairground up halfway along accompanied by some bars. If you walk all the way down, there are even more bars and restaurants. An evening stroll through there in the Summer is a sheer joy. It was great when the World Cup was on. They put up these huge screens and showed all the evening kick offs. It was a cracking atmosphere and it seemed as though it was a party every night. I didn't see any trouble down there all Summer.

There's a couple of small fishing boats with signwriting moored up here too. These guys use their boats as their businesses; running commercial fishing excursions out on the channel, usually lasting half a day or the full day, depending what their customers have booked. They seem to be quite popular – particularly with stag do's I think – and they can carry about 10 guests (on top of the crew), leaving space for around 6 cool boxes of beer and drinks! I have seen several blokes get off these boats after several hours at sea looking pretty green in the gills – and some even needing to get carried off!

There's a couple of nice restaurants at the top of the marina too. Both top end eateries, generally filled with an older clientele. Car park full of brand new, top end German cars. And some Jaguars. Mostly couples dining, the husbands will tend to wear a Hugo Boss polo shirt and trousers, finished off with a Henri Lloyd sailing jacket. The wives are normally resplendent in a few thousand pounds worth of Mulberry handbag and Louboutins.

From my apartment I can see all these things. The bridge. The restaurants. The fair in the Summer. The boats. It's a nice place to live, especially for someone who lives on their own. As I do. My apartment is on the end block, out of 5 x three storey blocks. On the third storey. My balcony is on the side of my building, so I can see the moored boats on the water to the left, and to the right, the pavement runs underneath me.

It is a vibrant, exciting area. From about April to early October there is always something going on. When I look out from my balcony, I see colour and movement everywhere. I can always hear feint music in the background – usually acting as the accompaniment to somebody's social occasion. If I pop to the nearby café, it is always filled with people 'like me'. Liberal minded, capable of intelligent conversation, polite. I can smell the food wafting across from the restaurants and can picture the freshly steamed mussels and seabass with a soy glaze being served up. I can only remember the weather being sunny at this time of year – though of course it could not always have been. But that's how I remember it. It gives me a warm feeling thinking about it.

Then November arrives, and like a vacuum, sucks the colour out of everything. What it leaves behind resembles a greyscale, newspaper cartoon version of our happy little community. Formerly buoyant with life, now seemingly uninhabited. Every year I count down the days until winter passes, and the whole area bursts back to life.

However, this year I will have to wait longer. Not sure how much longer, but maybe even until next winter. It will certainly be a while yet before the bars and restaurants are able to re-open and draw people down. Before the boats are allowed back out on to the channel. The summer fairground is certain to be cancelled this year. All major sporting events, which always draw people down here to watch it in a bar overlooking the marina, have already been postponed indefinitely. Nobody can charter the fishing boats – there is just no chance for people to stick to the 2 metre social distancing guidelines on board. It was looking pretty grim at one point, but over the last two weeks, I had reason to feel more uplifted and optimistic.

Outdoor daily exercise was permitted, even being encouraged, and the marina gave people a fantastic location to carry this out. As a result, there were still lots of cyclists, joggers and walkers using the footpaths, although it had a very different vibe. There were not as many families around, for one. The play park had been locked up. People now gave each other a wide berth, some of them turning quicker than Lionel Messi was capable of when they spied another person on the same trajectory! Nobody was stopping to admire the beauty of their surroundings anymore. The beauty of the nature before them. Nobody was stopping to stroke somebody else's dog and to remark what a 'handsome boy' they were.

The change was palpable. Tension replaced relaxation. Hastening replaced meditating. Even from my vantage point on my third storey balcony, anyone who inadvertently made eye contact appeared to panic, and abruptly look away. It reminded me of John Carpenter's movie, 'The Thing'. People treated each other with much undue suspicion.

I was spending a lot of time on my balcony at the moment. I had been furloughed from my administration job at a local washing line manufacturing company, which meant that I could not partake in any work for my company and simply had to sit and wait for the lockdown to be lifted so that I could return to work. It was only me and my cat, Charles, so the 80% pay guarantee I got from the government was adequate to pay the bills and feed us. With my apartment being an open plan one-bedroom studio, I spent a lot of time on my balcony. Apart from my daily 30-minute walk, I spent most waking minutes out there. Watching the world (not) go by.

I had lived her for about five years now, since my divorce went through, and whilst I loved it here, I missed one thing about my marital home (of 21 years). In the corner of the garden I had created a small vegetable patch. It's so silly, but in my mind, I had always imagined myself by now being happily married, living in a small cottage, looking forward to retiring in a few years and mindfully watching over, and tending to, a small vegetable patch. These were a few of many things that had never quite come to pass that – 20 years ago – I had imagined would have. The outcome I did get was unexpected, but it hadn't worried me. I was comfortable, and happy in my own skin. With my own company. Still, it is funny to think back about the person I thought I was going to become.

Our marriage had broken down. No specific unpleasant event, we just didn't share any interests, or converse in a meaningful manner anymore. In 25 years of marriage, people can change. I can honestly say that we are both good people. I think that we truly respected one another too much to hold the other one back from being content, with themselves, and the world around them. We both wanted to be honest with ourselves. The branches of our tree had simply grown in completely different directions; further and further away as time went on.

We had no children, and had paid off the mortgage, so we split everything 50/50. We shook hands (no - we actually did shake hands!) and went our separate ways. It was a very simple, amicable affair. Nothing was contested. When our house sold, I bought this studio apartment from my share of the proceeds, and I understand that he bought a small house somewhere in the valleys near his elderly parents. We had never spoken since – there had been no need to. However, he did add me as a friend on Facebook quite recently and gives my photographs of the marina the occasional 'like'. Likewise, if he posted about his parents or the fortunes of his beloved rugby club, I would return the favour. I tried to be strategic with my likes – important to know where the line was; can't be overzealous about it. He probably thought the same way. Like I said, there was still plenty of mutual respect.

There had been lots written in the media, or by social commentators, about the effect isolation could potentially have on people. How it could adversely affect the mental health of those who had not reported any mental health issues before this. In fact, it was a growing concern, and rightfully should be. Lockdown has been described as 'The worlds biggest psychological experiment', suggesting that the psychological toll on people will result in a secondary epidemic of burnouts and stress related absenteeism in the workplace thereafter. Some predicted that the worsening of mental illness could persist for years after the pandemic. Parallels were drawn between this crisis and the aftermath of the 9/11 attacks.

Some of the vulnerable groups identified are those who live alone, and the elderly. Now I'm definitely in the former category, though I would like to defer my acceptance to the latter group for the moment thanks! I've still got a few years before I even get my bus pass. This sounds like something an old person would say, sure, but I truly think age is a state of mind. In fact, I see so many much younger people these days who are far more uptight and tense as they attempt to scramble up the greasy pole. Worrying themselves into an early grave, all the while with something to prove. I like to have a drink in the bars with friends. I like to go to watch stand ups, gigs. I think that when the younger generation detect any sense of self awareness in a person, they instantly dismiss it as 'being old', and everything that stereotype encompasses. They should realise that self-awareness is the gift of getting older and try and learn from it. Laughing at yourself. Not afraid of being embarrassed. Not being embarrassed in the first place! Your skin has thickened.

Most of the time, honestly, I was fine. It would probably be worse if I couldn't experience the outside world at all because I had no garden, or because it wasn't wise for me to leave the house. Perched up on my small balcony, I could see the comings and goings of others. Hear the sounds of the birds. Feel the fresh sea air on my face. There is no doubt in my mind that it helped me cope with the situation tremendously – to the point, dare I say – that I enjoyed certain moments of it. It gave me time for reflection, as well as reminding me that I was still part of a society. Reminded me of humanity.

I reflected a lot on my marriage - the vast expanse of my memories is during this period. No regrets as such, they don't work and are not good for anyone. But I do have a kind of sadness about this time. For both of us too, not just me. That we didn't fulfil the early promise. I reflected about my childhood too. Or what I could remember. I really can't remember much before the age of ten at all. I have a few memories I can recall as photo stills – my favourite teddy bear - Pop, a bowl of strawberry ice cream, a sandy beach or my beautiful Mothers smiling face – but I am not sure if I can count them as memories. They could be the products of my imagination, or even dreams since I cannot remember the context of any of them or how the events actually played out. That makes me sad. I have some photos, but not enough. I want to call my brother to talk them through with him as he was older than me, but I can't as he no longer exists. It's ok. Everyone you love is going to die. I am old enough to understand and respect this.

Maybe I did need the sunshine and colour to return after all.

Sunshine and colour to flood back into my world.

Now I feel silly about the direction this goes in (guess I'm not old).

As I arrived at this point in my thoughts, sat on my balcony nursing a now cold cup of tea, I glanced down to the pavement as a movement caught my eye off in the horizon. It was a chap on his daily exercise coming toward my block. He was doing one of those funny fast walking techniques where they sort of walk on the side of their foot very swiftly. I observed this unusual walk as he got closer and closer. I figured I would be prepared to respond should he greet me in some way, as many passers-by did when I was sat outside.

As he got nearer, I could see, he was a man of similar age to myself. He was in good shape – very lean, with his nylon shorts showing off quite a muscular pair of calves. It was a warm afternoon, so the rest of his outfit consisted of a

163

running shirt made of the type of shiny material that disperses sweat more effectively. He had a very distinguished white beard, and his sporty sunglasses were across the top of his head holding back an impressive mane of white hair that grew down to just below his ears. Now I am only mentioning this, as in retrospect it is pertinent to my story. These were just typical observations you could visually make in a second of any passer-by. Spending this much time on the balcony, I have become a people watcher par excellence – I'm not some kind of stalker!

He had just about arrived level to my balcony and my gaze had begun to return to the pavement behind him, when Charles – who unbeknownst to me – was sitting inanimately underneath my outdoor bistro table, leapt out, gave off a piercing hiss and began furiously swiping at a passing bee. My karma instantly shattered, and I too leapt up, and in doing so, accidentally flung my teacup off the side of the balcony. As I quickly realised what had happened, I was aware of my teacup smashing on the pavement below.

The cat slunk off into the apartment with a guilty, and slightly embarrassed, look on its face when it realised it had given me the shock of my life. I took a deep breath, and sat down again, shaking my head. That teacup was part of my favourite set of four. It had come from an artisan craft fayre held at the local farmers market twice a year. I loved attending, always prepared to buy some of the wares, but never seemed to find anything I wanted. Apart from these! Before I had the presence of mind to look over the side to witness the terrible fate of my favourite teacup, I heard a voice.

"Thank God it had gone cold."

I looked over, and the fast-walking man was stood below me looking up. His shiny shirt seemed to be splattered with something.

"I'm so sorry. My cat frightened me." I immediately knew that sounded a bit stupid.

"Why, didn't you know you had one?" the man shouted back. I gave a little more thought to my next response.

"Could you maybe push the broken china to the side with your foot and I'll bring a dustpan and brush down?" I asked.

"Don't be silly. You stay up there where it's safe, and I'll sort it out."

Whilst this was a kind offer, I didn't see how he could. It had broken into a hundred pieces – some of them very small.

"Do you have a dustpan and brush with you?" I asked. I was not sure if he realised I was not being serious. He laughed.

"At all times! You never know when someone is going to throw a teacup full of cold tea at you while you are out on a run."

"I thought it was called walking?" I shouted back. The man was friendly, and the exchange was amusing me. It was the longest conversation I'd had outside of a supermarket in about two weeks.

"As I am walking at less than 4 miles per hour, it is legally classified as a walk – albeit a very brisk one if you wanted to be pedantic." He smiled as he finished the sentence. He seemed to have a lovely warm smile, although I was about 45 feet away, so I couldn't be entirely sure!

"In case you couldn't tell, I was joking and so no, I don't have a dustpan and brush," he continued.

Once again, I asked him to push it all to the side with his shoe, and I would be down shortly to clean it up properly. He wouldn't hear of it though, so after a few attempts I suggested to him that I would throw it down to him, and he could clean it up, put the broken china in the bin and leave the pan and brush near the communal front door.

"No chance. Not risking that, he replied.

I asked him what he meant by that.

"I'm not risking you throwing more things at me from that balcony. I got off lightly with the teacup – next time I might not be so lucky."

"Well the only other way is for me to come down there then."

"No," he was firm. "This is a lockdown, and I am not asking a lady to breach the lock down and sweep up in the street when I am already stood down here, right now, and can do it."

I am glad I was 45 feet away right now, as if we were any closer, he may have seen my coy grin. And I may have been blushing slightly too.

"Do you have some string. Or maybe some knitting wool?" he asked.

"Whilst that is a very assumptive question, I actually do have some wool I can use, but let me assure you, it is not for knitting."

Now he flapped around for his words a bit.

"Please don't think I was suggesting anything…"

"Just be lucky I don't have any knitting needles I can throw down there like spears. Wait there a moment please."

I went inside and got my dustpan and brush and found a ball

of wool. It was for knitting actually, but I didn't do it very often, so it was sort of true.

The dustpan and brush had a small hole in the top of the handle – perfectly positioned to allow me to thread the wool through and tie a knot in it.

"Are you still there?" he cheekily called up as I re-emerged with my dustpan and brush ready to have their first go at abseiling down the side of my block.

"Right, I'm lowering it down now." I began letting out a few inches of the wool at a time, and slowly but surely the dustpan and brush edged their way down the side of the building.

"Okay got it," he called up when it eventually reached the bottom. I felt a tug on the wool as he untied the dustpan and brush.

I watched him kneel down on the pavement and swept up all the broken bits of china into the pan – all the while whistling 'Smile' by Nat King Cole. Once it was all swept up, he walked to a nearby litter bin, and emptied the pan into it.

"Thank you." I called down.

"It's my pleasure. But you are not getting this dustpan and brush back."

Caught off guard, I replied, "Why not? Wasn't that the point of me lowering it down so you could return it?"

"Nope. I am holding this dustpan and brush to ransom."

I laughed and asked him what he could possibly want.

"Well I have my only running jersey covered in tea, and my washing machine has broken down. I can't get a new one delivered until a week Wednesday."

Oh dear, that was awkward.

"I would happily wash it for you, but how will you get home?"

He smiled again, and as he indicated with an outstretched arm and fore finger, he replied, "I only live 500 yards down the street and in the block right at the other end. I can run there and be home in a minute, don't worry."

I offered to bring down a jumper or something he could use, but he wouldn't hear of it.

"Look, Ill tie it to this piece of wool, you pull it back up and when you've finished with it, you can lower it back down to me, and I will let you have your dustpan and brush back, agreed?"

I laughed and, after shaking my head at the absurdity of it, I nodded and said, "Alright then – send it up."

In a flash, he whipped off his jersey and stood there topless as he began fashioning it into a bundle with the wool securing it. He seemed to know a thing about tying knots. Perhaps a keen sailor himself, or had he been in the military? Or maybe he was just a boy scout with a prolific memory. You could see he was lean when he had his shirt on, but now he had removed it, I could see what excellent shape he was in. Older now, I could see that he would have once had a muscular physique, with a very defined pair of pecs. His skin had not gone leathery, and it made him look ten years younger. As I was looking, I realised I had missed something he had said.

"I'm sorry what was that?"

"I said - ok pull her up then," he chuckled.

Right, ok, pull the wool up. I pulled it up slowly.

"Okay, I'm pulling it up."

It felt like a scene out of Rapunzel.

"Can you go any faster? I am quite chilly stood still."

I increased the pace I was hauling the shirt up until it appeared over the balcony.

"Ok got it."

He gave me the thumbs up, and shouted, "Great, I'll see you tomorrow," and with that, he 'fast-walked' off up the road, bare chested, with my dustpan and brush. I smiled as I watched him go and took his shirt inside to go straight into the washing machine. I glanced at it briefly before I put it on a 40-degree wash, and it didn't look like tea had splattered it; looked more like some kind of blackcurrant drink. 'That's strange,' I thought, 'must be the material,' as I stuffed it in the machine and switched it on.

The next day, I woke up with a strange little 'wiggle' of excitement in my stomach. I put it down to the fact that it was simply so long since I'd had any kind of meaningful social interaction, any break from the mundane had awoken a small part of me. A part of me that had forgotten.

I skipped breakfast (I only ever had toast anyway) and got dressed – putting on my favourite floral blouse and even a bit of make-up. I knew I had some tissue paper in my craft box, so I dug it out, and used it to wrap the carefully folded running shirt in it; to make it look like when you buy a brand new shirt in a fancy department store. I had a few hours until I expected to see my 'extortionist', so once I had tied the wool around the shirt so I could let it down, I made some more tea and sat out on the balcony.

I kept reminding myself that this was so silly and innocuous, but I could not help myself feeling…. excited to see him. Once again, I wrote it off as any break from the norm would be something to look forward to, but could it have been a sixth sense? Nonetheless, it was a strange, almost forgotten feeling. I tried to think about what I was experiencing in more depth. I couldn't give it a name, but I was experiencing 'something' mentally - and physically too. Some endorphins had been released.

As dramatic, and intense as it sounds, I am sure it was the sensation of feeling alive. And I don't mean alive in the context of 'I'm not dead', I mean alive in the sense of having a sense of purpose and meaning to my day. Even if it was ridiculous - even puerile in some ways.

As that thought passed through my mind, "No" verbally burst from my mouth. My subconscious must be scolding me – probably for being too harsh on myself. No – there was nothing wrong with these feelings, and it was not anything to feel embarrassed about. In the circumstances of lockdown that we were in, it was the most normal thing in the world to feel this way. It reminded me that there were others out there that I had something in common with; a connection.

All morning I fussed. I found myself unable to simply sit, drink tea and observe the surroundings, or complete a crossword. I was what my Mother (rest her soul) would have called 'potching'. It was a very Welsh expression. I imagine it is derived from 'pottering'. My Father (rest his soul) was a notorious 'potterer', and I would describe both this and potching in the same way. The best description I can think of, is when one occupies themselves, in a desultory, but pleasant enough way.

So, whilst my tea towels didn't need to be folded too precisely and put back in the drawer in order of colour, it kept me busy for a few moments, and I had a fairly nice outcome at the end of it, I suppose. Similarly, when I dusted *behind* each picture I had hanging on the wall – I don't suppose it was altogether necessary? Nobody could see it, and to be honest, I didn't get many visitors at the best of times. But it gave me a very brief, very (very) mild feeling of satisfaction and is my home better for it now? I think so.

And if I'm brutally honest the dinner mats and coasters didn't need to be steamed cleaned and cleaned up, but....

As I worked my way through the latest round of potching, I heard someone calling from the street below.

"If anyone can hear me - I have your dustpan and brush. I am ready to negotiate."

I put the mats down, stood up straight, brushed down the wrinkles out of my flowery dress, and straightened up my glasses. I marched over to the balcony and paused just before I came into view.

'Christ, not too keen – slow down,' I thought.

Momentarily: "Ah, there she is. I was starting to think you were going to keep my shirt."

"Don't worry," I shouted back down, "your shirt is safe. I need proof of life on the dustpan and brush?"

He had both arms around his back, appearing to be clutching something. He smiled, and brought around the arm with my dustpan and brush in.

"Ta-da."

"Is it unharmed?"

He chuckled – I think gratified at how much I was buying into the funny little scenario he had dreamt up.

"They are fine. Now lower down the shirt to me first."

"I will do. I can see you need it back as a matter of urgency," I said, referring to the fact that he was wearing an illuminous green running shirt today with a large red parrot across the front.

He was now laughing. "What a cheek. I told you that was my favourite shirt."

I reached on to my coffee table and picked up the bundle with the wool attached.

"Ok now, nice and slowly," he offered as instruction.

I complied with this request and teasingly lowered it down, inch by inch. He exhibited some exaggerated winces and grimaces each time is nudged into a wall on the way down. As though it was some kind of high value, fragile item.

"Steady, steady."

When it got to around his eye level, he seized it, snapping the wool, and feverishly tearing the tissue paper open. Upon sight of the shirt, he hugged to his chest tightly.

"I thought I was never going to see you again!" he choked.

I was laughing hard on the balcony watching this man – whose name I still did not know – with this RSC level of performance – kneeling in the street on the pavement. I can't even recall Kenneth Branagh's Hamlet demonstrating such intensity when expressing relief.

Eventually, he suddenly must have realised that the performance needed to draw to close. I saw him glance at some other windows on the apartment block. It could have been that I wasn't his only audience. Although it felt like it. From up there it felt like it was just the two of us on earth now.

"The dustpan and brush, if you please."

He looked up at me and nodded sagely.

"You have kept your word. I will keep mine."

He slowly got to his feet, keeping his eyes on me and the little nodding thing going. The dustpan and brush were tied to the piece of wool through the eye in the same way they were lowered down. Once the knot was tightened, he firmly tugged the length of wool twice to signal it was good to be wound back up, and stood back a pace, standing to attention like a member of military personnel. He raised his hand to the side of this head into a salute as the items raised up into the air.

Once received in hand, I made a show of inspecting the items – holding them up to the light, licking my thumb and rubbing the pan, that kind of thing. Once 'satisfied' I gave one firm nod – over-exaggerating it so it could be seen from many feet below. He nodded back at me and lowered his hand.

"This shirt is being retired now. I will never wear it again, for I always want it to smell and look this way. You will simply have to get used to my parrot shirt."

I didn't know what to say or how to react to this. It was of course tongue in cheek, but still was an overt compliment towards me, and I didn't want to brush it away as jesting. I wanted to hold on to it, and not dilute or dismiss it. I just gave a big smile instead. He performed a quite exquisite bow and took his leave. Walking backwards at first, so he was able to continue to look up at me, before eventually turning and fast walking off into the distance.

As I said earlier, this was two weeks ago, and I can honestly say that I have woken up with more zest, and vigour every day since. I would have considered my state of mind as 'fine' before – and I considered myself relatively happy. Certainly, content. Bored and a bit lonely maybe, but it was a situation I had accepted. Everyone was in the same boat, and we just had to get through this and come out the other side. It was like the interval of life – except there were no ice cream concessions to distract us. Looking back, I think I was lonelier that I had perhaps realised.

In the days since, I have seen him every day fast walking past my balcony. Whereas it used to be more sporadic, he has settled into a routine now where he comes by my block at almost exactly 1pm every day. I am normally there waiting to say hi. On a few occasions it has been raining and I have waited indoors. On those occasions, he has called out to me. Something like, "Washing Goddess – art thou there?" or "Dustpan lady. Where is thee?"

We've had a few proper conversations too. He has asked me half a dozen times if there is anything he can get me from the shops. I can sort this kind of thing out myself, although he did get me a punnet of fresh strawberries from the farm shop that was a bit out of my way to travel to. I buzzed the door open, he left it just inside at the ground floor entrance and he went off (they were amazing).

I found out his name too! I should mention that. A few days after having my dustpan and brush returned, he asked me if I'd used it yet, chuckling to himself. I had used but didn't understand what he was getting at. Later that evening, I inspected it more closely. I hadn't noticed, but written on the underside of the grey handle, in a fine nib permanent marker, he had written (very neatly) 'If lost, please return to Paul, 1 Seaport Way'. I smiled. Paul.

And that's it. That is near enough all that has happened to date. Sorry if I lead you to believe it would be the romance of the decade you were hearing about. It couldn't be – I've never even stood within 3 feet of the man.

But we talk every day. Nothing too taxing. Started off as jokey banter, but we do manage to have some sensible conversation too. I've got to know a bit about him. He recently retired when he passed his accountants business over to his son to run. Five years ago, he was widowed, and since retirement he couldn't bear to be in his marital home all alone. He took up fast walking in this time, and has taken part in several races, and fun runs.

We've talked about meeting up for a proper conversation when this is over – maybe even a glass of wine. I am sure this will happen once we are out of the woods with this pandemic. And in a funny way, it is making time pass even quicker. I have something exciting to look forward to. Something that I cannot predict how is going to go.

I've ordered him a new shirt to use too! I was thinking of putting together a treasure hunt that ultimately leads him to the package in the bush below my balcony. I've already written out the first sign to put up by the restaurant as he is coming back down. It's a big sheet of white A1 paper that I've stuck to a fibre broadband cupboard, which says, "FAO PAUL – THE PARROT SHIRT WEARING, FAST WALKING MAN – DON'T OUTSTAY YOUR WELCOME, IT COULD COST YOU." I was thinking that this should lead him to the next clue on the pay and display machine in the car park.

Having read that back, I may need to make it more obvious that it's inviting him on to a treasure hunt. It'll be clear to him that it is written by me, but it still sounds somewhat threatening. Hmm – he could well second guess himself after reading that. I'll re-think it.

It's just nice to be able to even consider these things though. I look forward to our daily chat. Amongst all this madness, I feel lucky. I know I've made a new friend at the very least; a companion. And I feel as though the friendship will outlast the lockdown.

That has to make it all worthwhile, for me.

You have to snatch whatever happiness you can, whenever you can, while it's there. And I intend to try.

Colleague Update

Going live in 3, 2, 1….

Good Afternoon everyone.

I hope you, and all your family and friends, are keeping well in these most unusual of times and thanks for watching.

It's extremely encouraging to see so many of you tuning in every week to my business update – live from my home office. This is the sixth weekly YouTube broadcast I have done now, and I can see that we still have more than 300 people watching. I take that as a positive sign that everyone is keen to find out what's happening, and when they can return to work.

Well as you will all know, the Government still have not decided to re-open non-essential retail, and really, to suggest a date would be nothing more than speculation at this stage. What we do know is that the pandemic finally appears to be under control with the infection rate appearing to have already peaked, and it is now dropping.

We also know that the furlough scheme, whilst a superb mechanism for protecting businesses against mass redundancies and the collapse of the economy, will be costing the Government billions and billions of pounds, and that it will be essential to kick start the economy again as soon as possible so they can start paying for some of it.

The longer we hang back on the side-lines, the more difficult it becomes to fund this, and the longer it will take to recover from.   Of course, first and foremost in our thoughts is the safety for all of our customers, and staff. With this in mind, we are already planning sweeping changes in our businesses in terms of process and the way our stores will look, and we will not be returning to work until we are happy that we can sufficiently mitigate and manage this risk to ensure everyone's safety.

Paying attention to Government recommendations, we have produced an array of signage and material to install in our stores – and with the help of our senior management teams – we will begin this process this week in readiness.

As some examples, we will be having large arrows stuck on the floor to direct our customers around the stores, and thus helping prevent people from colliding into one another. There are posters urging people to observe and respect our social distancing programme, and upon your return to work, we will be adapting your roles to help us enforce good practice, and a healthy, safe environment.

This will mean the manning of 'sanitation stations' throughout the store. The constant cleaning of hard touch surfaces with anti-bacterial spray – particularly around the till and in the changing room areas. Toilets will be manned to ensure a 'one in, one out' system is adhered to.

I'm sure you have seen some of the Perspex screens used when visiting your local supermarket or shops. We will have these installed at till points, and facemasks will also be provided.

Of course, whilst we are planning to re-launch our businesses in earnest, it would be disingenuous not to acknowledge the elephant in the room, which is feverishly being discussed in the media. The threat of the loss of jobs.

As much as anything, part of my role is trying to manage this threat. Every action that I am taking has one ultimate goal, and that is the preservation of jobs. But we are not immune from the threat of job loss. All the predicted difficulties that are being forecasted by industry and financial commentators will apply to us, and as such, there are no guarantees.

I cannot stress enough that when we do get back to work, we will all have to be fully committed, and all fully accountable for getting this business back into a viable trading position. That means you will be asked to do things that perhaps you didn't do before. You may be asked to be flexible in your approach to shifts – and I will take a dim view of anyone who refuses to be after a period of months where they have not been in work.

There is no job that is beneath your 'official' job title. If, to mitigate risk, we need to do some additional cleaning then I will expect anyone – regardless of position – to embrace this and carry it out. There will be no place for anyone in this business – or any business as we go forward – who has a 'that's not my job' mindset.

In due course, we will gradually un-furlough people to match the rise of business demand, but if there are staff who are not carrying their own weight, then we will re-furlough you, and a re-evaluation of your position could well be necessary.

The job market is sure to be pretty bleak in our field in the immediate future, and I would urge you all to keep this in the forefront of your mind.

Nobody wants to be out of work in this climate, and….my apologies, I think that was my daughter you may have been able to hear in the background, calling me.

I'M DOING MY YOUTUBE ADDRESS.

Sorry about that. Um, so yeah, it will be critical to adapt and embrace this new way forward and to do everything you can to help get this business back up and running so we can thrive again…sorry…hang on, I'm just going to call down the stairs to her…and then shut the door!

Oh – here she is. Colleagues – allow me to introduce you to Rachel. Rachel – my colleagues and team. You've just caught me in the middle of my YouTube business update broadcast. Just advising everybody of all the new measures we have taken to ensure that when we re-open, our stores will be safe, and of course all the new processes that we will have to learn to adapt to.

Yes…. I'm live to around 300 colleagues right now.

Yes, I am – I've been doing it every week from the third week of lockdown to keep in touch with everyone.

With all my staff.

It tells you underneath the video how many….

AH BUGGER! The bloody internet signal has dropped out again. Always the bloody same. I'll just have to reset it. I'm sure that most of them will click the link again to finish hearing the broadcast when they realise what has happened.

It is! If I lose internet, then it will show zero watchers.

Yes, it does!

What the hell are you talking about??

It can't be…..

What…. no. When?

A year ago?

We…. well what happened?

Totally closed? How many people?

Everyone?

Why couldn't I save them?

My God. And……what about me?

So, what do I do now?

A rest? How long must I rest for?

How will I know when I'm better?

And Greater Became the Divide

[An excerpt from the textbook, 'The Death of Democracy', © JP Public Press, first edition produced in 2045 by Face-books, reproduced with kind permission]

When we try to analyse the root causes that contributed to the breakdown of unity and social cohesion in society in what is now widely known as the 'Information Era' (or 'iAge'), we can see how rapidly divisions within the human race grew exponentially, and how individualistic rhetoric exploded in the 2010's – powered by the rise and rise of social media.

Prominent commentators, and experts of their day held differing views of the most impactful stimulus that drove a permanent wedge through society as it then existed, but they were all in general agreement that there were several major factors, at home and globally, during the period of 2015 to 2022.

Continuously growing socio-economic inequality – fuelled by the challenges of mass migration into Western countries coupled with the inadequate provision for refugees;

The UK's withdrawal from the European Union, commonly referred to as 'Brexit', and the subsequent five-year depression: an economic catastrophe that had occurred as a direct result of the 2020 pandemic;

Political disharmony to the extent that agreement or concurrence across party borders became a forgotten ideal (until the passing of the National Interest Act in 2037 established a permanent one-party system);

The global reckoning on racism had only served to draw more clear lines between different demographic groups, to the point that reconciliation or compromise was no longer possible;

The urgent need to fundamentally address climate change following the predicted rising sea levels. With the benefit of hindsight at the time of writing, we know that the warnings were very real – as cities all over the world, such as Miami and Venice would attest.

A common way that peoples' differences manifested themselves was in the dramatic increase in violence on the streets. The initial good intentions that would spark protest after protest were almost always hijacked by those with more darker motives, inciting hostility, and open aggression towards anyone not sharing their view - or authority figures. Riots frequently broke out. Police would be attacked. Shops would be looted. And buildings would be set alight and razed to the ground by the treacherous savages in our midst.

It brought major cities to its knees on an almost daily basis, effectively rendering them no-go zones, which in turn crippled the economy even further. One by one, industry and other commercial operations vacated these cities, leaving behind many squares miles of what became ghettos. Rampant inflation devalued the pound to almost nothing.

Outside major cities, in surrounding commuter towns and housing estates, people barricaded their doors. Too afraid to leave their homes; terrified about the soaring crime rate that was spreading toward them at breakneck speed. Visiting a supermarket for food supplies once or twice a month was a perilously dangerous expedition. Even after it was made mandatory for supermarkets to employ armed guards to stand sentry outside their stores, just the journey there could be fraught with danger. Parents feared for their children's lives.

All schools eventually closed – many became commandeered by entire communities of squatters; spending their days taking highly addictive illicit drugs bought with the ill-gotten gains of their criminal activities. These schools were often located centrally in their communities, which allowed these vermin to poison them at their very core.

As we now know, it is now a fact, universally acknowledged, that democracy does not work, but in the late 2020's, unbelievably, this was a notion that some still challenged. Following the historic 'Bunker Debates' of 2035, our glorious leaders, voted for, and granted extraordinary powers to deal with the state crises, to the designated magistrate of their choice. And thus, began the reign of the Honourable Joseph Robinson.

A former member of the national guard specialising in intelligence, skilled orator and sometimes even artist, Robinson had all the credentials to establish order and prosperity again in society. A state of emergency was immediately declared which established 7pm to 8am curfews which was enforced by the army who were permanently deployed on to the streets. It was a necessary step to arm all soldiers, and they were given a clear 'shoot to kill' directive under the 'Balance of Probabilities Law 2036' should two warnings to return to ones' home be ignored. The law gave them immunity from subsequent prosecution providing that no less than two colleagues could corroborate the story. The fact that not one peace bringing soldier was ever convicted of an abuse of power demonstrates the high level of integrity amongst these men and women, despite the high levels of dissident casualties in the first two years.

Protests and public gatherings of more than two people from different households were banned as the government sought to wrestle back control from mob rule and to make a promise to its peace loving citizens about the freedoms it would enjoy in future as a result. There were several instances during the summer of 2036 (*see Chapter 10: 'Bloodbath of the Anarchists'*) whereby the enemies of the state attempted to disrupt society's journey back to peaceful times, masquerading under the guise of defending 'liberty'. These large-scale demonstrations were met with immediate and sudden force. Claims from the protestors that they would be unarmed and peaceful were thankfully ignored, as evidence gathered from the scenes in the aftermath, proved their wicked and duplicitous intentions beyond any doubt. The death tolls for several of these events, although high, were proven to have not been in the tens of thousands as some of the fake news, peddled by underground commentators would sensationalise at the time.

In 2036, it became clear that the road to peace and freedom would be a process that took several years, and so to ensure the long-term progress of this programme, Robinson decreed that all election processes would be suspended until further notice – suggesting it could be several years before being reinstated. At the time of writing, we still embrace and believe in our leader, Robinson, wholeheartedly.

A state sponsored TV channel was set up where Robinson would take time to update the public in a weekly address, personally, ensuring this hour-long broadcast became the most watched TV serial in history. Other channels were permitted to run as normal, subject to heavy taxes and fines that were introduced on any overtly non-patriotic, or transgressive and socially unhelpful content they produced and/or broadcast. Broadcast journalists and their entire chain of command could also be subject to imprisonment for serious breaches of this nationalistic principle.

Capital punishment was reintroduced in the UK, over 70 years after the death penalty was abolished. The most common reason for invoking this level of punishment was the newly installed 'Anti-Treason' laws. Freedom from the law-making shackles that the European Community had placed upon the UK had seen these new decrees being passed in just a couple of months. It was indeed this same law that had seen Mike Penny tried, convicted, and sentenced to death for. Penny had originally been the leader of the opposition party – voting against installing Robinson as leader – and was a vocal opponent of a one-party system. Video footage had been obtained of Penny by Robinson's Personal Guard (a task force squad that was set up to carry out confidential operations set directly by Robinson – aka the RPG) holding clandestine meetings with convicted dissident activists. Under the Anti-Treason law, he was sentenced to death by lethal injection on 24th December 2036.

National pride intensified further in 2037 with the passing of the National Interest Act. One of the major facets of this was that borders closed entirely to immigrants. The numbers of people seeking to settle in our glorious country had dramatically dropped year on year in the last decade following increased measures to discourage anyone from travelling here who could not contribute to the rebuilding of our society. This was the final step to ensure that our country became the proud fortress it is today.

Destroyers patrolled the waters predominantly facing mainland Europe, and would not hesitate to turn any vessel back, whether is was another boat or an overcrowded inflatable dinghy. Refusal to cooperate was met with two warnings, and then a show of force from armed officers. Many of these boats used to have women and babies onboard, so as a rule of thumb, they eventually complied before the situation escalated. Anyone thinking of making the journey eventually got the message. If they did manage to arrive on our shores somehow, it was instant imprisonment.

When specific skill sets were short, and there was a requirement to import them, the candidates were screened on a microscopic level. When they arrived, they would effectively be placed under a house arrest, whilst their backgrounds were extensively checked. Who they associated with. Their personal history. Their friends and families, and what they did for a living. Any political messages they have ever posted on social media. And on, and on. This would ensure that the very best candidates were introduced into our new society. Once passed to the Governments satisfaction, they would be extremely well looked after, and given a house (often one which had been seized from a convicted criminal, with ownership passing to the Government) and a well-paid job. In the early days of screening to this level, there were several validations of this excellent process which lead to the imposters being tried as enemies of the state.

This book discusses further aspects of this law in Chapter 12 (*'National Interest Act: A portrait of the perfect society'*) and how it helped shape our future – providing opportunity to all our citizens.

This Act forms the very cornerstone of our society, and we must pay homage to the brilliant innovative mind of Joseph Robinson for having the original vision.

Our country is strong. Our economy is growing. Civil disobedience is at an all time low. Parents know that their children will have a future.

From War we acquire Peace.

From Slavery we acquire Freedom.

From Ignorance we acquire Strength.

Afterword

It would be remiss to put a book together centred around the lockdown of 2020 without mentioning the heroic efforts of the NHS and all of the other key workers.

Their selfless acts and incredible bravery throughout this uncertain time is what has kept the country going.

For what it's worth, I would simply like to offer my personal thanks to them all.

A Request

G. G. Howells is a Welsh writer of short stories. 'Narratives From The Lockdown' is his first published book.

If you have enjoyed this book, then please consider leaving a review on Amazon.

If you have any other feedback or suggestions, then they will be gratefully received at the following email address:

info@gghowells.com

Many thanks